Student Activity Guide

Careers in Focus:
Family and
Consumer Sciences

Lee Jackson, CFCS
Maryville, Missouri

Publisher
The Goodheart-Willcox Company, Inc.
Tinley Park, Illinois

Introduction

This *Student Activity Guide* is designed for use with the text, *Careers in Focus: Family and Consumer Sciences*. It will help you understand and remember the facts and concepts presented in the text. It will also help you apply what you learn and successfully plan for your future career.

The activities in this guide correspond to the chapters in the text. Reading your text assignment provides all the information needed to complete the activities. Try first to complete them without referring to the text. Later, you can look at the text to finish any sections of the activities that you did not complete. At that time, you can also compare your answers with the information in the text.

Most of the activities have no "right" or "wrong" answers. Their purpose is to encourage your personal analysis and individual expression. Other activities such as matching exercises have "right" answers. Follow the directions carefully at the beginning of each activity and do your best to complete them accurately.

Planning a career sounds like a big challenge, and it is. Dividing the career-planning process into a series of manageable steps, however, will prepare you to make one of the most important decisions in your life—your future career. The pages of this *Student Activity Guide* are designed to take you through these important steps in an interesting and fun way. Good luck and happy career planning!

International Standard Book Number 1-56637-883-4

3 4 5 6 7 8 9 10   03   06 05 04

Contents

4

Part IV
Family and Consumer Sciences Careers

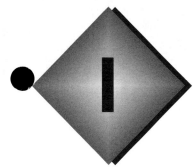

Thinking Ahead— Work and the Family

The Homemaking Role

◆ **Activity A**

Chapter 1

Name _____

Date _____ **Period** _____

List 10 homemaking tasks in the spaces below, and determine who in the household should perform them. Using *M* for mother, *F* for father, *S* for son, and *D* for daughter, write all the letters that apply to each task in the adjacent space. Then answer the question that follows.

Tasks	Individual(s) Responsible
1.	
2.	
3.	
4.	
5.	
6.	
7.	
8.	
9.	
10.	

11. Do you believe that some homemaking tasks should be performed by only one sex? Explain.

_____

_____

_____

_____

_____

The Many Benefits of Work

◆ **Activity B**

Chapter I

Name_____

Date _____ Period _____

Read the descriptions of the 10 individuals below and determine what motivates them to work. For each case, select the top three influences and number them *1*, *2*, or *3*. Then answer the questions that follow.

	Motivating Factors						
	Work ethic	Income	Social needs	Identity	Self-esteem	Physical and mental outlet	Independence
Example: A mother of small twins works Saturdays to earn extra Christmas money.	2	1					3
1. A doctor specializes in a new medical field.							
2. A high school coach strives to keep his football team number one in the league.							
3. A retired senior volunteers several hours weekly at the local library.							
4. A car mechanic has a reputation for reliable work.							
5. A teen stocks grocery shelves on weekends.							
6. A local television reporter has a popular morning news show.							
7. A company president expands the business to new markets.							
8. A chef opens his own restaurant.							
9. A teacher plans to return to school for an advanced degree.							
10. A person with a well-paying job makes wooden toys in his spare time to sell at craft shows.							

11. Which motivating factor was selected least often? _____

12. Who might be motivated by that factor? Explain. _____

_____

_____

_____

Family Structures and Work

◆ **Activity C**

Chapter I

Name_____

Date _____ **Period** _____

Define the five basic family structures. Then write one work-related concern or challenge that particularly affects each.

◆ ◆ ◆

1. **Nuclear Family**

   A. Definition: _____

   _____

   B. Work-related concern: _____

   _____

◆ ◆ ◆

2. **Single-Parent Family**

   A. Definition: _____

   _____

   B. Work-related concern: _____

   _____

◆ ◆ ◆

3. **Stepfamily**

   A. Definition: _____

   _____

   B. Work-related concern: _____

   _____

◆ ◆ ◆

4. **Extended Family**

   A. Definition: _____

   _____

   B. Work-related concern: _____

   _____

◆ ◆ ◆

5. **Childless Family**

   A. Definition: _____

   _____

   B. Work-related concern: _____

   _____

Attitudes About Men, Women, and Work

◆ **Activity D**   Name_____

   Chapter 1   Date _____ Period _____

Read each statement in the chart below and place a check in the column that best represents your opinion. Then answer the question that follows.

	Strongly agree	Somewhat agree	Somewhat disagree	Strongly disagree
1. Women with young children should not work outside the home.				
2. Mothers instead of fathers should stay home from work to care for sick children.				
3. Fathers as well as mothers should be allowed to take a work leave when the family has a new baby.				
4. Men and women who hold full-time jobs should divide the child care chores evenly.				
5. Men and women who hold full-time jobs should divide the housework evenly.				
6. Taking care of aging parents is a job that should be shared equally by adult sons and daughters.				
7. If both husband and wife work, her income should be reserved for "extras."				
8. There should be equal pay for equal work in all cases.				
9. When a wife makes more money than her husband does, it tends to cause arguments.				
10. Men should have slightly higher wages since they have to support families.				
11. Men can be nursery school teachers and nurses.				
12. Women can be construction workers and truck drivers.				
13. Male managers are better than female managers at making job decisions.				
14. There are fewer personality conflicts on the job when a male is in charge.				

15. How do you believe work at home and on the job should be divided? _____

_____

_____

_____

Balancing Career, Personal, and Family Roles

◆ **Activity E**

Chapter 1

Name_____

Date_____ Period_____

When career, personal, and family roles are balanced, a person's life can be illustrated as a circle with three equal parts. (See the example.) The individuals described below, however, do not have their lives in balance. For each case, divide and label the circle to reflect the individual's situation.

Example: This circle shows a balanced life.

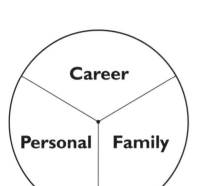

1. Pam takes a one-month work leave to stay at home with her newly adopted son.

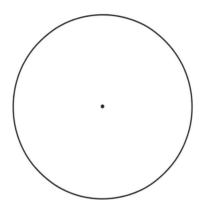

2. Michael, a recent college graduate, devotes many evenings and Saturdays to become familiar with his new job.

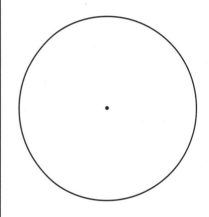

3. Jamal, the father of three, is spending evenings at school to get the training he needs for a better job.

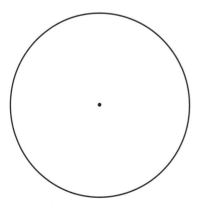

4. Jamie decides to put her education on hold and reduce the number of hours she works outside the home while raising her two preschoolers.

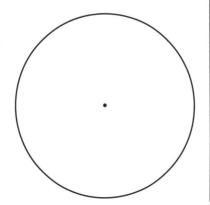

5. Blake, who is employed full-time, works out at the local gym almost nightly instead of spending time with his wife and teenage son.

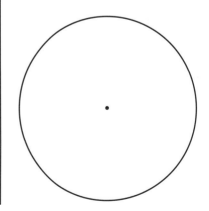

Life and Career Messages

◆ **Activity F**

Chapter I

Name _____

Date _____ Period _____

Record the messages you have received directly or indirectly from peers and adults regarding the life and career decisions listed below.

Topics to Decide	Messages from Peers	Messages from Adults
1. Whether to stay single		
2. Whether to get married		
3. Whether to have children		
4. Whether to hold a job and raise a family at the same time		
5. Whether to graduate from high school		
6. How to find a job that pays well		
7. How to pursue a fulfilling career		

Deciding What Is Right for You

Interests and Abilities Inventory

◆ **Activity A**

Chapter 2

Name_____

Date _____ **Period** _____

Knowing your interests is a good start to determining the right career. For each topic below, identify your major interests and abilities, and name related jobs that might appeal to you. Then answer the questions that follow.

Topics	Interests	Abilities	Related Jobs
School courses			
Hobbies or leisure activities			
Sports activities			
Volunteer activities			
Favorite TV shows			
Favorite magazines			

(Continued)

Name_____

1. What is the definition of *interest?* _____
    _____
    _____

2. What is the definition of *ability?*_____
    _____
    _____

3. What are your three primary interests? _____
    _____
    _____

4. What are your three strongest abilities?_____
    _____
    _____

5. Of the jobs you listed, which one appeals most to you? _____
    _____

6. How would your interests and abilities be used in this job? _____
    _____
    _____
    _____
    _____
    _____

7. What are your three weakest abilities? _____
    _____
    _____

8. Based on your weaknesses, what jobs should you avoid? _____
    _____
    _____

9. Why is it difficult to separate interests from abilities? _____
    _____
    _____
    _____
    _____

10. When an individual has an ability in a given area, does he or she have an interest in that area, too?
    Is the reverse true? Explain. _____
    _____
    _____
    _____

Traits Revealing Personality

◆ **Activity B**

Chapter 2

Name_____

Date _____ Period _____

People generally are happier working at jobs that suit their personality. From the following list of traits, circle the 10 traits that best describe you. Then answer the questions below.

Personality Traits

adventuresome	creative	inventive
aggressive	demanding	irritating
ambitious	dependable	kind
angry	disagreeable	mature
assertive	dramatic	moody
boastful	energetic	outgoing
calm	enthusiastic	polite
caring	friendly	quiet
cautious	generous	rude
cheerful	greedy	sarcastic
competitive	helpful	selfish
confident	honest	sincere
cooperative	humble	shy
courageous	humorous	thoughtful
considerate	inquisitive	upbeat

Of the traits you circled, which three will be most helpful in obtaining the job you want? Explain your answer. _____

_____

_____

Which of your negative traits will hinder you most in obtaining the job you want? (Consider all the traits you possess, even those unlisted.) Explain your answer. _____

_____

_____

Comparisons of Personal Priorities

◆ **Activity C**

Chapter 2

Name_____

Date _____ Period _____

Common factors that motivate people to work are valued differently by different individuals. For each of the following factors, read the two statements that represent extreme views and circle the number that best represents your view. Then answer the question below.

Money

1	2	3	4	5
Money is the most important job consideration.				Money is the least important job consideration.

Independence

1	2	3	4	5
I want to work alone.				I want to work with others.

Leadership

1	2	3	4	5
I want to make all the decisions pertaining to my job and be held accountable for them.				I want someone to direct me in my work.

Variety

1	2	3	4	5
I want each day and each challenge to be different.				I want a job with a predictable routine.

Prestige

1	2	3	4	5
I want my coworkers to view me as someone special.				I don't want my coworkers to view me as someone special.

What do your personal priorities indicate regarding your future job choice? _____

_____

_____

_____

_____

_____

Recognizing Aptitudes, Abilities, and Personal Priorities

◆ **Activity D**

Chapter 2

Name_____

Date _____ Period _____

Define *aptitude, ability,* and *personal priorities* in the appropriate spaces below. Then read each of the following descriptions and write the appropriate letter in the preceding space to indicate whether it refers to an aptitude, ability, or personal priority.

Aptitude	Ability	Personal Priority
Definition: _____	Definition: _____	Definition: _____
_____	_____	_____
_____	_____	_____
_____	_____	_____
A.	**B.**	**C.**

_____ 1. Playing a piano well without taking lessons.

_____ 2. Playing a piano well after taking lessons.

_____ 3. Wanting a good education.

_____ 4. Walking and running.

_____ 5. Possessing outstanding reasoning powers.

_____ 6. Riding a bicycle.

_____ 7. Preferring individuality over conformity.

_____ 8. Typing on and operating a computer.

_____ 9. Praising honesty and truthfulness in children.

_____ 10. Performing surgery.

_____ 11. Respecting religion.

_____ 12. Understanding foreign languages easily.

_____ 13. Drawing detailed images from memory.

_____ 14. Overcoming the fear of speaking in public.

_____ 15. Understanding quickly the relationships between geometric shapes.

_____ 16. Believing in freedom.

_____ 17. Performing arithmetic quickly and accurately in your mind or on paper.

_____ 18. Flying an airplane.

_____ 19. Playing championship tennis at an early age.

_____ 20. Respecting people in authority.

Personal Priorities and Career Goals

◆ **Activity E**   Name_____

   Chapter 2   Date _____ Period _____

Complete each of the following statements by circling the career choice that does *not* match the stated personal priority.

1. If you highly value <u>working with adults to keep families together</u>, you probably would *not* want to be a(n):

   A. interior decorator   B. social worker   C. marriage counselor

2. If you highly value <u>interacting with people frequently during the workday</u>, you probably would *not* want to be a:

   A. physician   B. recreation director   C. writer

3. If you highly value <u>living in a large city</u>, you probably would *not* want to be a(n):

   A. teacher   B. orchard grower   C. accountant

4. If you highly value <u>adventure and excitement</u>, you probably would *not* want to be a(n):

   A. peace corps volunteer   B. insurance salesperson   C. forest ranger

5. If you highly value <u>education and learning</u>, you probably would *not* want to be a:

   A. cashier   B. vocational counselor   C. teacher

6. If you highly value <u>working outdoors</u>, you probably would *not* want to be a(n):

   A. resort manager   B. landscaper   C. office receptionist

7. If you highly value <u>frequent travel</u>, you probably would *not* want to be a(n):

   A. airline pilot   B. nurse   C. truck driver

8. If you highly value <u>using your hands to create beautiful objects</u>, you probably would *not* want to be a:

   A. data processor   B. jeweler   C. dressmaker

9. If you highly value <u>working with numbers</u>, you probably would *not* want to be a(n):

   A. bookkeeper   B. math teacher   C. art teacher

10. If you highly value <u>promoting good health to others</u>, you probably would *not* want to be a(n):

   A. nutrition counselor   B. exercise instructor   C. mapmaker

Learning and Deciding About Careers

3

Working with People, Objects, and Ideas

◆ **Activity A**

Chapter 3

Name _____

Date _____ Period _____

Most jobs involve people, objects, and ideas, but in different degrees. For each position listed below, write *1* in the column that represents the primary focus of the job and *2* in the column that represents its secondary focus.

Job	Job Focus		
	People	Objects	Ideas
1. Example: Teacher	1		2
2. Florist			
3. Airline reservation agent			
4. Forest ranger			
5. Vocational counselor			
6. Interior decorator			
7. Writer			
8. Nurse			
9. Bookkeeper			
10. Clothing designer			
11. Social worker			
12. Botanist			
13. Architect			
14. Printer			
15. Salesclerk			
16. Chef			
17. Restaurant host or hostess			
18. Veterinarian			
19. Dentist			
20. Computer repair person			

Matching Candidates to Job Openings

◆ **Activity B**

Chapter 3

Name_____

Date _____**Period** _____

Read the following descriptions of two job openings and three potential candidates. Then answer the questions below.

Job Openings

Job #1   requires a professional skilled in working with the public to demonstrate new foodservice products, answer questions, and negotiate sales to schools, companies, and businesses. The person must be outgoing and enjoy working with people.

Job #2   requires a professional to test new food products in the laboratory. The person must be accurate and have an extensive science background. He or she will work with a team of three on special assignments.

Job Candidates

Linda   is a conversationalist, enjoys meeting people, and is skillful with her hands. She works best in a high-pressure environment where she can influence change. She dislikes working in one place and is happiest when working on several projects at once.

Gerri   works best with small groups. She is very thorough and precise in her work and excels at anything related to chemistry. She makes friends easily and people trust her judgment.

Stephanie   has spent several years with a food company and has an extensive food marketing background. She prefers to work alone on assignments. She just finished writing a cookbook and enjoys reporting food industry news for the local newspaper.

---

1. Which candidate is the best person to select for Job #1? Explain._____

   _____

   _____

   _____

   _____

   _____

2. Which candidate is the best person to select for Job #2? Explain._____

   _____

   _____

   _____

   _____

   _____

Trends Affecting Future Jobs

◆ **Activity C**

Chapter 3

Name_____

Date_____ **Period**_____

For each job prediction below, identify a related trend discussed in your text and write it in the appropriate space. Then answer the question below.

Job Predictions	Related Trends
1. Tours, excursions, and recreational programs for seniors will expand.	
2. More people will conduct business from their homes.	
3. Greater numbers of computer repairers will be needed.	
4. Information providers will channel product news electronically to homes.	
5. The home remodeling and building industry will grow.	
6. Jobs involved with providing clothing, shoes, and other products to the exercise and sports markets will increase.	
7. Nutrition counseling services and jobs for fitness instructors who specialize in programs for seniors will increase.	
8. More jobs will open for telephone order-takers and personnel that assist customers electronically.	
9. Housecleaning and errand services will expand.	
10. More scientists who can develop lowfat food products will be needed.	

Based on your observations, which job trend is showing the greatest impact? Explain._____

_____

_____

_____

_____

_____

_____

Head Start on Employability

◆ **Activity D**

Chapter 3

Name _____

Date _____ Period _____

Skills useful in a future career can be gained from every type of work experience. For each part-time job listed below, identify three job skills that can be gained from the work experience and write them in the spaces provided.

Part-Time Jobs	Resulting Job Skills
1. Handling the phone and front desk of a doctor's office	A. _____ B. _____ C. _____
2. Working in the stockroom of a toy store during the Christmas season	A. _____ B. _____ C. _____
3. Assisting with child care activities in a nursery school	A. _____ B. _____ C. _____
4. Helping with the upkeep of outdoor facilities at a golf course	A. _____ B. _____ C. _____
5. Maintaining the office files for a local business	A. _____ B. _____ C. _____

Making Career Decisions

◆ **Activity E**

Chapter 3

Name _____

Date _____ **Period** _____

Read the following case studies and determine what career advice to give to Erica and Jason. Then answer the questions that follow each case.

Case 1

Erica was fascinated by colorful designs and interesting fabric textures even as a child. She spent many hours making outfits for her dolls and for those of her friends. Because of her love of fashion and clothing, she is considering a career in fashion merchandising. She will soon finish her third year of high school and has taken all the clothing courses offered. She has started to consider a journalism career, however, because she enjoys working on the school newspaper. In her spare time, she likes to sketch clothing designs. One aspect of fashion merchandising that she doesn't like is the constant contact with people because she prefers working alone. Erica has decided to go to college. She can take general courses for two semesters before declaring a major and specializing. She feels pressured, however, to make a career decision now because all her friends seem to know what they are doing.

---

1. What career would you recommend to Erica, based on the information above? _____
    _____

2. Which of Erica's interests matches the career you recommended? _____
    _____
    _____

3. Which of Erica's abilities and aptitudes match the career you recommended? _____
    _____
    _____

4. What job-related experience does Erica already possess? _____
    _____
    _____
    _____
    _____

5. Where can Erica get help in making a career decision? _____
    _____
    _____
    _____

6. What advice would you give to Erica about making a career decision now? _____
    _____
    _____

(Continued)

Name_____

Case 2

Jason, a junior in high school, cannot decide if he should go to college, to vocational school, or directly to a full-time job after graduation. His grades have been good, especially in his math courses. He originally planned to become an architect, but now he likes the idea of earning money quickly to buy a new car. His brother, who is three years older, went directly from high school to the construction industry and has a high-paying job today. Jason has always envisioned himself building structures—sometimes houses and, at other times, airports and office buildings. He likes to take raw materials and turn them into something useful and aesthetically pleasing. He spends countless hours experimenting with different materials to see which results in a better job. In fact, whenever special structures are needed for high school events, Jason helps construct them because his work is creative and reliable. He has taken all the building trades courses available and now must make a decision. Should he focus on acquiring more education after high school or on getting a good job with his brother?

---

7. What career would you recommend to Jason, based on the information above? _____

_____

8. Which of Jason's interests matches the career you recommend? _____

_____

_____

9. Which of Jason's abilities and aptitudes match the career you recommended? _____

_____

_____

10. What job-related experience does Jason already possess?_____

_____

_____

_____

_____

11. Where can Jason get help in making a career decision? _____

_____

_____

_____

_____

12. What advice would you give to Jason about following in his brother's footsteps? _____

_____

_____

_____

_____

Preparing for a Career in Family and Consumer Sciences

Career Moves

◆ **Activity A**

Chapter 4

Name_____

Date _____ Period _____

Match the career preparation activities in Column A with the related career areas in Column B. The items in Column B can be used more than once.

Column A

_____ 1. Making and decorating birthday and anniversary cakes.

_____ 2. Learning to make hotel reservations.

_____ 3. Sewing draperies and curtains for the faculty lounge.

_____ 4. Helping disabled people prepare meals for their families.

_____ 5. Teaching the elderly in a nursing home new board games.

_____ 6. Sewing costumes for the school play.

_____ 7. Helping people confined to their homes handle their personal care.

_____ 8. Assisting children with projects at summer camp.

_____ 9. Working as a host or hostess in a restaurant.

_____ 10. Supervising young children playing in the school yard.

_____ 11. Helping seniors with poor eyesight to read and write letters.

_____ 12. Conducting tours of your school for visitors.

_____ 13. Sewing sleepwear for residents of a nursing home.

_____ 14. Learning how to give worn furniture a new look.

_____ 15. Helping with bathing patients at a convalescent center.

_____ 16. Assisting with the Meals on Wheels program for seniors.

_____ 17. Playing games with young children in a nursery school.

_____ 18. Learning to handle housekeeping jobs for a hotel.

_____ 19. Sewing doll clothes for children in a hospital.

_____ 20. Recommending color schemes for the new school cafeteria.

Column B

A. child care services

B. clothing production and services

C. food production and services

D. interior design and home furnishings services

E. hospitality and tourism services

F. family and community support services

G. services for the elderly

Opening the Door to the Future

◆ **Activity B**

Chapter 4

Name_____

Date _____ Period _____

The door to the future leads to many choices in family and consumer sciences. Match each course/program title listed by the door with its subject area in the table. Determine if the course/program is general or occupational and write its letter in the appropriate space. Then answer the questions that follow.

Course/Program Titles

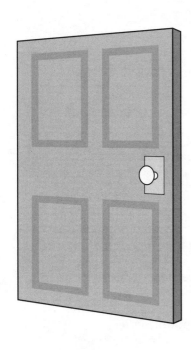

A. Child care guidance

B. Child care management and services

C. Child development

D. Clothing and textiles

E. Consumer and family economics

F. Consumer education

G. Environmental design management, production, and services

H. Family and community support services

I. Family and individual health

J. Family living

K. Food preparation

L. Food production, management, and services

M. Foods and nutrition

N. Home management and resource development

O. Housing

P. Human nutrition

Q. Institutional maintenance, management, and services

R. Interior design

S. Interior design services

T. Parenting

U. Services for the elderly

V. Textile and apparel design

W. Textile and clothing production, management, and services

(continued)

Name_____

Subject Area	General Course/Program	Occupational Course/Program
1. Child development and early childhood education		
2. Family studies and human services		
3. Consumer and resource management		
4. Hospitality, tourism, and recreation		
5. Textiles and apparel		
6. Nutrition and wellness/food science and technology		
6. Environmental design		

7. For what does a general program in family and consumer sciences prepare students? _____

_____

_____

8. For what does an occupational program in family and consumer sciences prepare students? _____

_____

_____

Understanding 2 + 2 Programs

◆ **Activity C**

Chapter 4

Name_____

Date _____ Period _____

Test your knowledge of Tech Prep programs by selecting the term that correctly completes each sentence and write its initial in the preceding space.

_____ 1. The primary objective of a Tech Prep program is preparing students for:
   A. High school graduation.
   B. Enrollment in college.
   C. Careers.

_____ 2. Tech Prep programs are called 2 + 2 because:
   A. They combine two years of high school courses with two years of higher education.
   B. They are completed in the four years required for a high school education.
   C. They combine two technical courses with two high school courses.

_____ 3. Tech Prep programs include three key elements:
   A. Math, science, and English courses.
   B. Applied academic courses, technical training, and partnerships with employers, parents, teachers, and counselors.
   C. Class work, schoolwork, and homework.

_____ 4. The Tech Prep sequence of study usually begins:
   A. After high school graduation.
   B. In the junior year of high school.
   C. In the sophomore year of high school.

_____ 5. Tech Prep programs benefit the community because:
   A. Students are trained to develop the skills required by local and regional employers.
   B. Students must agree to work in the community for at least two years after graduation.
   C. Students must, in some way, repay any help that is provided by community employers during their training period.

_____ 6. Tech Prep programs teach job skills plus the following:
   A. Acceptable on-the-job behavior and the attitudes needed for working well with fellow employees.
   B. Supervisory skills.
   C. Military skills.

_____ 7. Students in 2 + 2 + 2 programs are enrolled in:
   A. Two Tech Prep programs.
   B. A four-year degree program that complements the 2 + 2 program.
   C. Two different schools.

_____ 8. In addition to students and teachers, the people involved in Tech Prep programs include:
   A. Parents and counselors.
   B. Staff from area employers.
   C. Parents, counselors, and staff from area employers.

_____ 9. After completing a Tech Prep program in a family and consumer sciences area, students are prepared to:
   A. Hold a job in a technical area.
   B. Continue their college education.
   C. Hold a job in a technical area, continue their college education, or both.

_____ 10. Most Tech Prep students find learning easier because:
   A. Classroom instruction is applied to the workplace.
   B. The courses are generally easier.
   C. The courses are generally shorter.

Career Preparation Choices

◆ **Activity D**   **Name**_____

   Chapter 4   **Date** _____ **Period** _____

For each career preparation option listed below, identify two important facts and write them in the space provided.

1. Professional Schools
    A. _____
       _____
       _____
       _____

    B. _____
       _____
       _____
       _____

2. Trade Apprenticeships
    A. _____
       _____
       _____
       _____
       _____

    B. _____
       _____
       _____

3. Home-Study and Correspondence
    Courses
    A. _____
       _____
       _____
       _____

    B. _____
       _____
       _____
       _____

4. Postsecondary Technical or
    Vocational-Technical Schools
    A. _____
       _____
       _____
       _____

    B. _____
       _____
       _____
       _____

(Continued)

Name_____

5. Community and Junior Colleges
   A. _____
      _____
      _____
      _____

   B. _____
      _____
      _____
      _____

6. Military
   A. _____
      _____
      _____
      _____

   B. _____
      _____
      _____

7. Colleges and Universities
   A. _____
      _____
      _____
      _____

   B. _____
      _____
      _____
      _____

8. Graduate Schools
   A. _____
      _____
      _____
      _____

   B. _____
      _____
      _____

Basic Skills for the Workplace

Let Me Count the Ways

Name_____

Date _____ **Period** _____

Think of a skill you possess that can be used in the workplace, such as operating a computer or writing a set of instructions. List three different ways to learn the skill and identify the advantages and disadvantages of each. Then follow the directions below.

A skill I possess now that can be used in the workplace is _____

_____

1. One way that a person can acquire this skill is _____

   _____

   A. Advantages of using this method _____

   _____

   B. Disadvantages of using this method _____

   _____

2. Another way that a person can acquire this skill is _____

   A. Advantages of using this method _____

   _____

   B. Disadvantages of using this method _____

   _____

3. A third way that a person can acquire this skill is _____

   A. Advantages of using this method _____

   _____

   B. Disadvantages of using this method _____

   _____

4. Which of the three methods described above most helped you to learn? Explain why. _____

   _____

   _____

   _____

My Learning Style

◆ **Activity B**   Name_____

  Chapter 5   Date _____ Period _____

Determine how well each of the following conditions and activities help you learn and place a check in the appropriate column. Then follow the directions below.

I learn best:	Yes	No
1. With little or no noise		
2. With quiet music playing		
3. With loud music playing		
4. With conversation in the background		
5. With a TV on		
6. By sitting in a comfortable chair		
7. By sitting at a table or desk		
8. By sitting on the floor		
9. By lying on the bed		
10. In an empty room or private area		
11. In a busy room or crowded area		
12. In a moving car or bus		
13. By taking notes while studying		

I learn best:	Yes	No
14. By underlining or highlighting key words or thoughts in the text		
15. By taking notes during class		
16. By reviewing notes frequently		
17. By participating in class discussion		
18. By role-playing		
19. By debating		
20. By making an oral presentation		
21. By preparing a written project		
22. By watching a live demonstration		
23. By watching films or TV		
24. With a hands-on project		
25. With a group project		

26. Which three conditions or activities most help you to learn? (You can include answers not stated here.) _____

    _____

    _____

27. Which two conditions or activities most prevent you from learning? (You can include answers not stated here.)_____

    _____

Take a Memo

◆ **Activity C**   **Name** _____

Chapter 5   **Date** _____ **Period** _____

Imagine that in two weeks construction will begin on the front entrance of your school, making it unusable for almost one month. As a member of the student advisory committee, you have been asked to write a memo to students, faculty, and school staff. It should explain what will happen, when, how long it will last, and what to avoid while work is in progress. The memo will be posted throughout the school. Compose your memo on a separate sheet of paper and transfer the final version below.

MEMORANDUM

DATE: _____

TO: _____

FROM: _____

SUBJECT: _____

_____

_____

_____

_____

_____

_____

_____

_____

_____

_____

_____

_____

_____

_____

_____

Put It in Writing

◆ **Activity D**

Chapter 5

Name_____

Date _____ Period _____

Recall a gift that you especially enjoyed receiving and write a short letter to thank the giver. Incorporate all the elements of a business letter except the typed signature. Compose your letter on a separate sheet of paper and transfer the final handwritten version below, placing the parts in the appropriate spaces.

*return address
date*

inside address

salutation

body

*complimentary
close*

signature

Fractions, Decimals, and Percentages

◆ **Activity E**

Chapter 5

Name_____

Date _____ Period _____

Write each number below in the following three forms: as a fraction reduced to its lowest denominator, as a decimal rounded off to the nearest hundredth, and as a percentage.

	Expressed as a		
	Fraction	**Decimal**	**Percentage**
1. one-half			
2. two-fifths			
3. two-thirds			
4. seven-tenths			
5. three-fourths			
6. two-sixths			
7. two-eighths			
8. five one-hundredths			
9. one twenty-fifth			
10. one one-hundredth			
11. ten one-hundredths			
12. six-sixteenths			
13. ten-twelfths			
14. four-fourteenths			
15. two-eighteenths			

Computer Alphabet Soup

◆ **Activity F**

Chapter 5

Name_____

Date _____ Period _____

Identify the letters in the soup bowl by writing each set in the blank in front of its definition. Then follow the directions below.

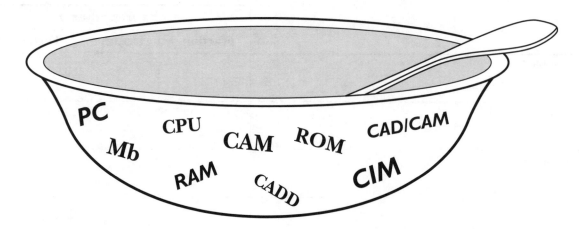

_____ 1. A personal computer.

_____ 2. The heart of the computer.

_____ 3. Information that has been permanently stored in the computer at the factory.

_____ 4. Information that is temporarily stored as it is being entered into the computer and processed.

_____ 5. A measure of a computer's RAM capacity.

_____ 6. A computer program, called *computer-aided drafting and design,* that automatically draws objects to scale or exact measurements.

_____ 7. A system in which machines set up manufacturing processes through computer commands.

_____ 8. A program using computer-generated designs to run manufacturing equipment.

_____ 9. A system in which computers are used to control the entire factory operation.

10. Explain computer input devices and output devices, and provide two examples of each. _____

_____

_____

_____

_____

_____

_____

_____

_____

Communication Skills

Clues to Body Language

◆ **Activity A**

Chapter 6

Name _____

Date _____ **Period** _____

For each example of body language below, describe one possible message it conveys and write it in the space provided. Then answer the questions that follow.

Examples of Body Language	Possible Meanings
1. Biting fingernails	
2. Smiling	
3. Shrugging shoulders	
4. Gazing into the distance	
5. Slapping the forehead	
6. Tapping fingers or a pencil	

(Continued)

Name_____

Examples of Body Language	Possible Meanings
7. Twisting hair or fingering jewelry	
8. Jumping up and down	
9. Slapping another on the back	
10. Chewing gum vigorously	
11. Nodding	
12. Shaking hands limply	
13. Slouching in a chair	

14. Is body language always a clue to what someone is feeling? Explain. _____

_____

_____

_____

_____

15. How does body language affect communication? _____

_____

_____

_____

_____

Analyzing Facial Gestures

◆ **Activity B**

Chapter 6

Name_____

Date _____ **Period** _____

For each face below, identify the emotion expressed and describe it in one or two words in the space provided. Then answer the question that follows.

1. _____

_____

2. _____

_____

3. _____

_____

4. _____

_____

5. _____

_____

6. _____

_____

7. _____

_____

8. _____

_____

9. _____

_____

10. _____

_____

11. _____

_____

12. _____

_____

(Continued)

Name_____

What types of body language clues besides facial gestures help you identify the emotions people are feeling? _____

_____

_____

_____

_____

_____

_____

_____

_____

_____

_____

_____

_____

_____

_____

_____

_____

_____

Practicing Positive Communications

Name_____

Date _____ Period _____

Using positive communication techniques, determine what you would do and say in each case below and write your answers in the space provided. You will want to make your point without hurting anyone's feelings.

	What Would You Do?	What Would You Say?
1. You are in an expensive restaurant and your entree arrives cold.		
2. The five-year-old you are baby-sitting insists on watching a horror movie.		
3. You dial the wrong telephone number.		
4. You want to go to a movie but your friends have already purchased concert tickets.		
5. You promised to rake your neighbor's leaves this weekend but you remember that school and family events will keep you busy both days.		

(Continued)

Name_____

	What Would You Do?	What Would You Say?
6. A classmate, wearing an unusual outfit and hairstyle, asks for your opinion of his or her new look.		
7. Your English teacher grades your report harshly, even though you believe it is a great improvement over your previous work.		
8. Your friends ask you to meet them at a place that has a bad reputation.		
9. A teacher that you have known for two years still doesn't remember your name.		
10. You leave food cooking in the microwave to answer the doorbell, only to find a stranger selling magazines.		

Speaking Directly

◆ **Activity D**

Chapter 6

Name_____

Date _____ **Period** _____

For each situation below, use assertive communication techniques to develop responses and write your answers in the space provided. Then create three of your own situations and appropriate responses for them.

Situation	Assertive Communication		
	When You:	**I feel:**	**Because:**
Example: The student who sits in your favorite spot in the cafeteria before you leaves crumbs and wrappers behind.	Leave a mess in the cafeteria	Angry	I have to use part of my lunch period to clean the table.
1. A classmate asks to borrow your notes.			
2. A group of students across the table from you in the library talk too loudly for you to concentrate.			
3. The student behind you constantly taps his or her pencil on the desk.			
4. Your friends forget to inform you of special weekend plans again.			
5. Your friend still has not returned an item you loaned over a week ago.			

(Continued)

Name_____

	Assertive Communication		
Situation	**When You:**	**I feel:**	**Because:**
6. The sibling who shares your bedroom leaves dirty clothes on the floor.			
7. Your friend signed you up for volunteer work after school without informing you.			
8. Your sibling leaves a mess in the kitchen and blames you for it.			
9. Your friend begs you to take a babysitting job that he or she accepted but now doesn't want.			
10. An acquaintance wants you to trade tickets for an important event so that his or her out-of-town guest has a better seat.			
11.			
12.			
13.			

Understanding Personal Management Skills

Identifying Management Skills

◆ **Activity A**

   Chapter 7

Name _____

Date _____ **Period** _____

For each personal management skill listed below, check the column that best describes how often you use the skill. Then answer the questions that follow.

Personal Management Skills	Never	Sometimes	Often	Always
1. Stays neat and well groomed.				
2. Dresses appropriately for all occasions.				
3. Gets enough sleep each night.				
4. Maintains a balanced diet.				
5. Completes all assignments on time.				
6. Prepares well for class.				
7. Arrives to class and appointments on time.				
8. Follows directions carefully from teachers and superiors.				
9. Does neat, thorough, and accurate work.				
10. Enjoys learning.				
11. Relates well with teachers and classmates.				
12. Sees problems as challenges instead of barriers.				
13. Manages time well.				
14. Devotes attention to detail.				
15. Attempts to do the best job possible.				
16. Avoids gossip and conflicts with classmates.				
17. Apologizes when wrong.				
18. Maintains a positive attitude.				
19. Accepts constructive criticism well.				
20. Takes responsibility for personal actions.				

(Continued)

Name_____

21. List two of your stronger personal management skills and explain how they will help you obtain job success. (You can list skills not mentioned here.)

A. _____

_____

_____

B. _____

_____

_____

22. List two of your personal management skills that need improvement and describe one way to strengthen each. (You can list skills not mentioned here.)

A. _____

_____

_____

_____

B. _____

_____

_____

_____

Understanding Self-Concept

◆ **Activity B**

Chapter 7

Name_____

Date _____ Period _____

Decide which of the three parts of self-concept explains each of the following items and write its number in the correct box below. Then follow the directions on the back.

1. Knowing and understanding yourself.
2. Viewing yourself mentally in relation to others.
3. Feeling good about yourself.
4. Recognizing what you do well.
5. Seeing yourself mentally in relation to other situations.
6. Know which skills you do not have.
7. Viewing yourself in your mind.
8. Liking who your are.
9. Being aware of your talents.
10. Seeing the real you in your mind.
11. Knowing your limits.
12. Believing that you are important.
13. Feeling that you have worth.
14. Forming a picture of yourself in your mind.
15. Recognizing when you need more information.
16. Expressing happiness or dissatisfaction with your self-image.
17. Seeing yourself as you believe others see you.
18. Appreciating who your are.
19. Developing a mental image of who you are.
20. Dealing with personal limitations.
21. Believing that you are significant.
22. Knowing when you need help.
23. Feeling that you are capable.
24. Creating a positive or negative picture of yourself in your mind.
25. Recognizing your skills.
26. Feeling pride in yourself.
27. Having confidence in yourself.
28. Forming a mental image of yourself.
29. Knowing how to use your skills.
30. Believing that you are valuable.

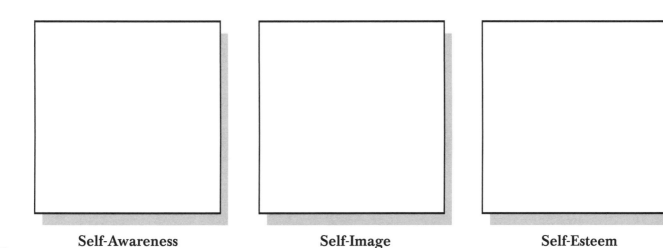

Self-Awareness   **Self-Image**   **Self-Esteem**

(Continued)

Name_____

31. Explain how self-concept influences a student's performance in school._____

_____

_____

_____

_____

_____

32. Is there a major difference in the way self-concept influences the student performance versus employee performance? Explain. _____

_____

_____

_____

_____

Managing Stress

◆ **Activity C**   **Name** _____

Chapter 7   **Date** _____ **Period** _____

Identify the stress management technique used in each situation below and write its corresponding initial in the preceding blank. Then follow the remaining directions.

Stress Management Techniques

A. Discuss the problem.

B. Maintain good health.

C. Exercise.

D. Relax.

E. Know your limitations.

_____ 1. Cleaning and waxing floors.

_____ 2. Smiling.

_____ 3. Playing music.

_____ 4. Talking with a friend.

_____ 5. Prioritizing your "to do" list.

_____ 6. Riding a bike.

_____ 7. Getting a good sleep.

_____ 8. Eating a nourishing meal.

_____ 9. Playing with pets.

_____ 10. Meditating.

_____ 11. Taking a needed nap.

_____ 12. Promising only what you can do.

_____ 13. Selecting healthy snacks.

_____ 14. Playing sports.

_____ 15. Reading for pleasure.

_____ 16. Rearranging a hectic schedule.

_____ 17. Writing to a pen pal.

_____ 18. Using humor.

_____ 19. Practicing yoga.

_____ 20. Enjoying the scenery.

21. Describe other stress-reducing techniques you use. _____

_____

_____

_____

_____

_____

_____

_____

_____

(Continued)

Name_____

22. Contrast two stressful situations in your life that required two completely different stress management techniques.

(Situation 1)_____

_____

_____

(Technique 1) _____

_____

_____

(Situation 2)_____

_____

_____

(Technique 2) _____

_____

_____

Dear Problem Solver

◆ **Activity D**

Chapter 7

Name _____

Date _____ Period _____

Imagine you are *Problem Solver,* author of an advice column for the local newspaper. Reply to the following letters by providing stress-management advice.

Dear Problem Solver,

I was sick on the day they explained the new computer system, and I can't seem to figure it out by reading the manual. My work is piling up. Any suggestions?

Sincerely,
On My Own

Dear On My Own, _____

_____

_____

_____

_____

_____

_____

_____

Sincerely,
Problem Solver

Dear Problem Solver,

I never seem to have any time for myself. I love the swim team and being the team captain. I learn a lot in the debate club and enjoy being the chairperson. Housework, homework, and classwork prevent me from spending time with friends. Help.

Sincerely,
Overworked

Dear Overworked, _____

_____

_____

_____

_____

_____

_____

Sincerely,
Problem Solver

Dear Problem Solver,

The person sitting next to me is really getting on my nerves. She chews gum loud enough for everyone to hear and keeps humming. Sometimes I could just scream!

Sincerely,
Frantic

Dear Frantic, _____

_____

_____

_____

_____

_____

_____

Sincerely,
Problem Solver

(Continued)

Name_____

Dear Problem Solver,

I described a very embarrassing incident about a classmate to my friend, and he promised to keep it a secret. Now I learn that everyone is talking about it. What can I do?

Sincerely,
Shocked

Dear Shocked, _____,
_____
_____
_____
_____
_____
_____
_____

Sincerely,
Problem Solver

Dear Problem Solver

I seem to be the last to find out about after-school plans that my friends make. Twice last week I missed them altogether. Do you think that my friends are purposely not including me?

Sincerely,
Left Out

Dear Left Out,_____
_____
_____
_____
_____
_____
_____
_____

Sincerely,
Problem Solver

Dear Problem Solver

I need more money and I can't see any way to get some fast. I am in desperate need of new shoes. My friends used to lend me money, but some say that I don't return it fast enough. What's the answer?

Sincerely,
Without Cash

Dear Without Cash, _____
_____
_____
_____
_____
_____
_____
_____

Sincerely,
Problem Solver

Setting Goals

◆ **Activity E**

Chapter 7

Name_____

Date _____**Period** _____

Setting goals becomes easier when you understand the goal-setting process. Consider a goal you have already accomplished–arriving to school on time–and identify the steps below that helped you to achieve the goal. Then repeat the steps of the goal-setting process, using a career-related goal.

1. Identify a specific goal: **<u>Arrive at school on time.</u>**

2. Set subgoals. _____

   A. _____

   _____

   B. _____

   _____

   C. _____

   _____

   D. _____

   _____

   E. _____

   _____

3. Identify resources. _____

   A. _____

   _____

   B. _____

   _____

   C. _____

   _____

4. Identify potential problems. _____

   A. _____

   _____

   B. _____

   _____

   C. _____

   _____

(Continued)

Name _____

5. Identify a specific career-related goal: _____
   _____
   _____

6. Set subgoals. _____
   A. _____
      _____
   B. _____
      _____
   C. _____
      _____
   D. _____
      _____
   E. _____
      _____

7. Identify resources. _____
   A. _____
      _____
   B. _____
      _____
   C. _____
      _____

8. Identify potential problems. _____
   A. _____
      _____
   B. _____
      _____
   C. _____
      _____

Group Effectiveness and Leadership Skills

Encouraging Teamwork

Select the interpersonal skill that is most needed in each example of poor teamwork below and write its letter in the preceeding space. Then answer the questions that follow.

Interpersonal Skills

A. Use empathy.

B. Make requests instead of demands.

C. Be willing to give and take.

D. Give and accept constructive criticism.

E. Avoid stereotypes and prejudices.

F. Have a sense of humor.

_____ 1. Personal differences prevent coworkers from working together to achieve a common goal.

_____ 2. The situation is so tense that coworkers cannot discuss solutions to problems.

_____ 3. A supervisor thinks and acts with total disregard to the feelings of her employees.

_____ 4. One person tries to order everyone around.

_____ 5. People are reluctant to express ideas because they know their thoughts will not be respected.

_____ 6. Unkind comments are made that focus exclusively on a person's shortcomings.

_____ 7. Assumptions, based on what is observed in one person, are made about an entire group of people.

_____ 8. A more relaxed atmosphere is needed to make coworkers feel comfortable enough to contribute ideas.

_____ 9. A person is humiliated in front of others by being called a total failure.

_____ 10. Coworkers are unwilling to listen to each other or make compromises to resolve differences.

_____ 11. Coworkers quit responding to a person who shouts orders to them and always expects immediate reaction.

_____ 12. A person knows that his friend is disappointed over a failed promotion but cannot understand why.

_____ 13. Some workers are distracted by the personality differences of other coworkers.

(Continued)

Name_____

14. Which interpersonal skill is the easiest for you to practice? Explain why._____

_____

_____

_____

_____

_____

15. Which interpersonal skill is the most difficult for you to practice? Explain why. _____

_____

_____

_____

_____

_____

Solving Problems at Work

◆ **Activity B**

Chapter 8

Name _____

Date _____ Period _____

Imagine that you are in charge of the department mentioned in the case study below. First, state the main problem, as you see it. Then check *yes* or *no* to each skill listed, depending on whether you would use it to try to resolve the problem. Explain your choices.

Case Study

One of your best friends worked for you, but suddenly transferred to another department last week. This was the third transfer in the last year by a new person who seemed to like the job and do excellent work. All gave unclear reasons for their fast departures. Now the staff is down to the five members who created the department 15 years ago plus you, a relative newcomer. Once again you have to spend time away from your real work to search for a new employee.

The main problem is _____

_____

_____

_____

_____

_____

Skills to Use			
	Yes	No	Explain
1. Focus on the current problem.			
2. Separate the person from the problem.			

(Continued)

Name_____

Skills to Use			
	Yes	No	Explain
3. Brainstorm and gather information.			
4. Use the decision-making process.			
5. Prioritize issues.			
6. Use creative thinking.			
7. Use constructive communication techniques.			
8. Resolve conflict.			

Good Leadership Qualities

◆ **Activity C**   **Name** _____

Chapter 8   **Date** _____ **Period** _____

Check the leadership qualities that good leaders have and those that you possess. Then answer the questions that follow.

	Leadership Qualities	
	of a Good Leader	That I Possess
1. Enthusiastic.		
2. Notice mistakes but not successes.		
3. Listen to others' opinions.		
4. Provide encouragement.		
5. Interrupt others frequently.		
6. Encourage teamwork.		
7. Take credit for others' work.		
8. Keep changing decisions.		
9. Make all the decisions.		
10. Share decision-making responsibilities with the group.		
11. Appear confident as a leader.		
12. Appear reluctant to be a leader.		
13. Avoid wasting time.		
14. Allow priviledges to friends.		
15. Admit to making mistakes when they occur.		
16. Make mistakes but never acknowledge them.		
17. Provide incomplete information or inadequate directions.		
18. Seldom listen to the concerns of others.		
19. Follow all the rules and sets a good example.		
20. Maintain good relationships with everyone.		
21. Pretend to know everything.		
22. Admit when more information is needed to make a decision.		
23. Know almost every aspect of the job.		
24. Welcome the opinions and ideas of others.		
25. Discourage others from discussing problems.		
26. Interpret even slight disagreements as authority challenges.		
27. Always give others credit for their work.		
28. Set goal that are beyond reaching.		

(Continued)

Name _____

29. Which three leadership skills do you feel are most important in a leader? (You can include skills not appearing in the list.) Explain why. _____

_____

_____

_____

_____

30. Which of your leadership skills needs the most work? Explain how you can perfect it/them. _____

_____

_____

_____

_____

_____

_____

_____

Assessing Student Organizations

◆ **Activity D**

Chapter 8

Name _____

Date _____ **Period** _____

Test your knowledge of the student organizations that your school offers by answering the following questions.

1. What student organizations does your school offer? _____

   _____

   _____

   _____

   _____

   _____

   _____

   _____

   _____

   _____

   _____

   ✓ BPA
   ✓ DECA
   ✓ FBLA
   ✓ FCCLA
   ✓ HOSA
   ✓ National FFA Organization
   ✓ Skills USA—VICA
   ✓ TSA

2. Which student organizations have you joined this year or in past years? Identify the main reason you joined each.

   A. I have joined _____

      because _____

   B. I have joined _____

      because _____

   C. I have joined _____

      because _____

   D. I have joined _____

      because _____

   E. I have joined _____

      because _____

3. What organizations do you plan to join in the future? Why?

   A. I will join _____

      because _____

   B. I will join _____

      because _____

   C. I will join _____

      because _____

(Continued)

Name _____

4. How does membership in school organizations relate to your future career goals? Name three benefits.

   Benefit 1 _____
   _____
   _____

   Benefit 2 _____
   _____
   _____

   Benefit 3 _____
   _____
   _____

5. If a good friend asked your advice in joining a student organization, which would you recommend? Why? _____
   _____
   _____
   _____
   _____
   _____

6. Is there any student organization that you would discourage others from joining? If so, which one? Why? _____
   _____
   _____
   _____
   _____
   _____

7. If you are a member of a student organization that works with the community, explain the additional benefits it provides. _____
   _____
   _____
   _____
   _____

8. What would you say to someone who has never joined a student organization? _____
   _____
   _____
   _____
   _____

Practicing Parliamentary Procedure

◆ **Activity E**

Chapter 8

Name_____

Date _____ **Period** _____

Use your textbook to convert the following comments into expressions used in formal meetings conducted with parliamentary procedure. Then answer the questions on the next page.

Informal Comments	Expressions Used with Parliamentary Procedure
1. "We have enough members present to start the meeting."	
2. "Let's get started."	
3. "What happened at our last meeting?"	
4. "Thanks a lot for correcting the report of our last meeting."	
5. "You can examine the financial report if you desire."	
6. "We need to hear from the regular committees."	
7. "We need to hear from the special committee"	
8. "We couldn't decide on the amount of dues at the last meeting and we're not prepared to discuss it tonight."	
9. "I recommend a weekend meeting."	
10. "I agree with the recommendation for a weekend meeting."	

(Continued)

Name_____

Informal Comments	Expressions Used with Parliamentary Procedure
11. "It's time to discuss the idea of a weekend meeting."	
12. "Who doesn't want a weekend meeting?"	
13. "Over half of the members vote for a weekend meeting."	
14. "Does anyone want to discuss additional topics?"	
15. "Let's end this meeting."	

16. Why is parliamentary procedure used?_____

_____

_____

_____

17. How might a meeting be kept orderly without using parliamentary procedure?_____

_____

_____

_____

_____

_____

The Job Search

Job-Lead Possibilities

◆ **Activity A**

Chapter 9

Name_____

Date _____ **Score** _____

Imagine that you are ready to enter the work world and begin searching for your dream job. On each line below, specify a person, place, or object that you would contact during your search and check the column that identifies the type of job lead it is. Then answer the questions that follow.

	Job Leads		
	Person	Place	Object
1.			
2.			
3.			
4.			
5.			
6.			
7.			
8.			
9.			
10.			

(Continued)

Name_____

11. How many of your job leads are people? _____

12. How many of your job leads are places?_____

13. How many of your job leads are objects? _____

14. If all 10 of the job sources you listed result in a dead end, what would you do next? Explain. _____

_____

_____

_____

_____

_____

_____

My Personal Data Sheet

◆ **Activity B**

Chapter 9

Name_____

Date _____ **Period** _____

Complete this personal fact sheet by filling in every item that applies to you. When finished, you can use it to prepare your resume and complete job application forms.

PERSONAL DATA SHEET

Name _____

Street address _____

City, state, zip _____

Telephone _____ Date of birth _____

Place of birth _____

EDUCATION

	Name	Location	Dates Attended	Date Graduated	Program Followed
Primary school					
Junior high school					
High school					
College					
Training school					
Other					

Degree(s) earned _____ Latest grade point average _____

WORK EXPERIENCE

Name of employer _____

Address_____

(street address)   (city)   (state)   (zip)

Telephone _____ Employed from _____ to _____

(mo./yr.)   (mo./yr.)

Job title _____ Supervisor _____

Starting salary _____ Final salary _____

Job duties_____

_____

Name of employer _____

Address_____

(street address)   (city)   (state)   (zip)

Telephone _____ Employed from _____ to _____

(mo./yr.)   (mo./yr.)

Job title _____ Supervisor _____

Starting salary _____ Final salary _____

Job duties_____

(Continued)

Name _____

_____

Name of employer _____

Address _____
        (street address)   (city)   (state)   (zip)

Telephone _____   Employed from _____ to _____
                                                   (mo./yr.)   (mo./yr.)

Job title _____   Supervisor _____

Starting salary _____   Final salary _____

Job duties _____

_____

_____

SKILLS _____

_____

_____

ORGANIZATIONS AND ACTIVITIES _____

_____

_____

HONORS AND AWARDS _____

_____

_____

HOBBIES AND INTERESTS _____

_____

_____

REFERENCES

Name _____   Title _____

Address _____

Home telephone _____   Work telephone _____

Name _____   Title _____

Address _____

Home telephone _____   Work telephone _____

Name _____   Title _____

Address _____

Home telephone _____   Work telephone _____

Preparing the Perfect Portfolio

◆ **Activity C**

Chapter 9

Name _____

Date _____ Period _____

Begin to prepare your portfolio by checking whether you do or do not have the items listed. Then provide answers to the following questions or statements.

My Portfolio

	I have.	I do not have.
Resume		
Biographical sketch		
Work samples		
Reports of special projects		
Photos		
Newspaper articles		
Letters of commendation		

(Continued)

Name_____

1. List the portfolio items that you do not have. _____
_____
_____

2. How might you obtain items over which you have little control, such as newspaper articles and letters of commendation? _____
_____
_____
_____
_____

3. Develop a plan for obtaining portfolio items for all the categories you listed in Statement 1. _____
_____
_____
_____
_____
_____
_____
_____
_____
_____
_____
_____
_____
_____
_____
_____

Writing a Cover Letter

◆ **Activity D**

Chapter 9

Name _____

Date _____ Period _____

Write a sample letter of application for your dream job, using the example on page 168 in your text as a guide. Then answer the questions that follow.

(Continued)

Name_____

Would you hire someone who wrote you this letter? Why or why not?_____

_____

_____

_____

_____

_____

_____

_____

_____

_____

_____

_____

_____

_____

_____

_____

Job Interviews

Plans for Looking Your Best

◆ **Activity A**

Chapter 10

Name_____

Date _____ **Period** _____

Describe below what teens should do to look their best for a job interview. Then answer the questions that follow.

Clothing Choices

1. Describe from head to toe what you would wear to a job interview. _____
   _____
   _____
   _____
   _____
   _____
   _____

2. Describe from head to toe what someone of the opposite sex should wear to a job interview._____
   _____
   _____
   _____
   _____
   _____
   _____

(Continued)

Name_____

Grooming Considerations

3. What grooming guidelines should job seekers follow regarding these categories?

   A. Hair:_____

   _____

   B. Face: _____

   _____

   C. Teeth: _____

   _____

   D. Hands and fingernails: _____

   _____

   E. Perfume, cologne, after-shave lotion: _____

   _____

Body Language

4. Identify four examples of body language that you should use during an interview and explain the importance of each.

   A. Example 1: _____

   Explain: _____

   _____

   B. Example 2: _____

   Explain: _____

   _____

   C. Example 3: _____

   Explain: _____

   _____

   D. Example 4: _____

   Explain: _____

   _____

Observing Interviewee Behavior

◆ **Activity B**   **Name** _____

Chapter 10   **Date** _____ **Period** _____

Imagine that you are a member of the organization's personnel department in charge of the initial interviews of all potential employees in the following cases. In the space provided, write how the behavior of
job candidates make you feel.

1. Brooke brings her two-year-old sister to the interview. _____

   _____

   _____

   _____

2. Josh stares out the window for the entire interview. _____

   _____

   _____

   _____

3. Ryan slowly strolls into the office after arriving five-minutes late. _____

   _____

   _____

   _____

4. Tiffany takes a stick of gum from her purse and offers some to you. _____

   _____

   _____

   _____

5. Courtney fumbles through her large purse, never finding the pen she thought was there. _____

   _____

   _____

   _____

6. Dale slouches in the chair and never smiles. _____

   _____

   _____

   _____

7. After introducing yourself to Jim, he calls you by the wrong name. _____

   _____

   _____

   _____

8. Shawna says, "I don't care what job I get, just as long as I get something." _____

   _____

   _____

   _____

(Continued)

Name_____

9. Jaime keeps fidgeting, trying to conceal her torn collar. _____

   _____

   _____

   _____

10. Randy wears dirty jeans and too much after-shave lotion to the interview. _____

   _____

   _____

   _____

11. Scott gives you a very limp handshake before and after the interview. _____

   _____

   _____

   _____

12. Kirby repeats everything you say. _____

   _____

   _____

   _____

13. Alan does not have an answer for over half of your questions. _____

   _____

   _____

   _____

14. Rhonda keeps fingering her long, dangling earrings._____

   _____

   _____

   _____

15. Curt arrives early, answers all your questions well, behaves politely, and leaves samples of his work

   with you. _____

   _____

   _____

   _____

Evaluating Fringe Benefits

◆ **Activity C**

Chapter 10

Name_____

Date _____ Period _____

Write the definition of *fringe benefit* and circle five benefits below that are most important to you. Then answer the questions that follow.

Definition of fringe benefit: _____

_____

1. Child care services

2. Educational opportunities

3. Exercise facilities

4. Friday afternoons off

5. Dental insurance

6. Investment opportunities

7. Life insurance

8. Medical insurance

9. Paid personal leave

10. Paid sick leave

11. Paid vacation time

12. Parental leave policy

13. Retirement plan

14. Sabbaticals

15. Are there any fringe benefits beyond this list that you would definitely want in a job? Explain. _____

_____

_____

_____

_____

16. What do you consider the most important fringe benefit? Explain. _____

_____

_____

_____

_____

17. What is the second most important fringe benefit to you? Explain._____

_____

_____

_____

_____

(Continued)

Name_____

18. If you found the job of your dreams, but it did not provide the two fringe benefits most important to you, would you take the job? Explain._____

_____

_____

_____

_____

_____

_____

_____

_____

_____

Learning from Interview Failures

◆ **Activity D**

Chapter 10

Name _____

Date _____ Period _____

Imagine that a job interview did not go well, and as expected, the job was not offered to you. For each of the categories that follow, identify at least two questions to ask yourself that will better prepare you for the next interview.

Interview Considerations	Questions to Ask
Example: My explanation of job-related skills, abilities, and talents	A. How well did I relate them to the skills needed for that job? B. Did I describe them in a way that convinces an interviewer that I am the best person for the job?
1. My arrival at the interview	A. _____ _____ _____ B. _____ _____ _____
2. My appearance at the interview	A. _____ _____ _____ B. _____ _____ _____
3. My body language at the interview	A. _____ _____ _____ B. _____ _____ _____
4. Communication skills I used at the interview	A. _____ _____ _____ B. _____ _____ _____

(Continued)

Name_____

Interview Considerations	Questions to Ask
5. My knowledge of the organization	A. _____ _____ B. _____ _____
6. My questions and comments to the interviewer	A. _____ _____ B. _____ _____
7. My grades on required tests.	A. _____ _____ B. _____ _____
8. My response to questions about salary and job expectations	A. _____ _____ B. _____ _____

Job Orientation

Preparing for My New Job

Name_____

Date _____ **Period** _____

Imagine that you will start work at your dream job next week. Begin to prepare by answering the following questions.

1. My greatest fear concerning a new job is: _____

   _____

   _____

   _____

   _____

   _____

2. My greatest hope for a new job is: _____

   _____

   _____

   _____

   _____

   _____

3. On the first day of work I will bring: _____

   _____

   _____

   _____

   _____

   _____

4. On the first day of work I will wear: _____

   _____

   _____

   _____

   _____

   _____

(Continued)

Name_____

5. Before I begin working, I need to buy: _____

_____

_____

_____

_____

6. Before I begin working, I must arrange to: _____

_____

_____

_____

_____

7. The impression I want to make on my first day is: _____

_____

_____

_____

_____

8. On the first day, I must remind myself to avoid: _____

_____

_____

_____

_____

Forming Company Policy

◆ **Activity B**

Chapter 11

Name_____

Date _____ Period _____

Imagine that you are the owner of a new business called Sweet Candy Company, which has office workers and factory workers. Form the personnel policy for your company by writing guidelines for each of the following areas of the employee handbook.

Sweet Candy Company
Employee Handbook

Hours of work

Breaks

Lunch time

Smoking

Dress code

(Continued)

Name_____

Sweet Candy Company
Employee Handbook

Sick leave

Excused absences

Unexcused absences

Vacation time

Pay periods and form of income

Termination procedure

Understanding Payroll Deductions

◆ **Activity C**

Chapter 11

Name _____

Date _____ Period _____

Refer to the check stub shown below to answer the following questions.

TOTAL HOURS	YOU EARNED AND WE PAID →				TOTAL		WE PAID OUT THESE AMOUNTS FOR YOU									NET AMOUNT		PERIOD ENDING
	REGULAR	OVERTIME					F. I. C. A.		FEDERAL WH./TAX		STATE WH./TAX		MEDICARE						
30	200	00				200	00	12	40	20	00	5	99	2	90			158	71	6/10

EMPLOYEE'S STATEMENT OF EARNINGS AND DEDUCTIONS. RETAIN THIS STUB FOR YOUR RECORDS.

ABC Company, Inc.   South Holland, IL 60473-1234

1. What is the gross pay? _____

2. What is the net pay? _____

3. How much was deducted for state tax? _____

4. How much was deducted for federal tax? _____

5. How much was deducted for social security? _____

6. What is the total amount of deductions? _____

7. What percentage of gross pay accounts for the deductions? _____

8. What is this person's hourly wage? _____

(Use the space below to figure the answers.)

(Continued)

Name_____

Are payroll deductions an advantage or a disadvantage to workers?_____

_____

_____

_____

_____

_____

_____

_____

_____

_____

_____

_____

_____

_____

Occupational Word Scramble

Name_____

Date _____ Period _____

Unscramble the letters beside each definition and fill in the blanks with the correct term relating to job orientation.

1. _ _ _ _ _ _   _ _ _ _ _ _ _ _ _ _
   s l e a u x   s e m a n t h a r s

   A form of employment discrimination, including any unwelcome sexual advances, requests for favors, or other sexual conduct.

2. _ _ _ _ _ _ _ _   _ _ _ _ _ _ _ _
   n e p l o n s e r   l i c o p s i e

   Company rules and regulations that outline the behavior expected of all employees.

3. _ _ _ _ _
   g a w e s

   Pay received for hourly work.

4. _ _ _ _ _ _ _ _
   t o m e r i v e

   Work on a job more than forty hours per week.

5. _ _ _ _ _ _
   r a l a s y

   Pay for work that is a fixed amount for a period or time, usually a year.

6. _ _ _ _ _ _ _ _ _ _
   s o m i s i n m o c

   Pay based on the number of units sold by an employee.

7. _ _ _
   p i t

   A certain percentage of money that customers leave for the person who served them.

8. _ _ _ _ _   _ _ _
   s o g r s   y a p

   The total amount of money earned during a pay period.

(Continued)

Name_____

9. _ _ _   _ _ _
   t e n   y a p

The amount of money left after all deductions are taken from gross pay.

10. _ _ _ _ _ _   _ _ _ _ _ _ _ _ _
    r a p l o l y   t o d e c i n u d

Money that is subtracted from a paycheck for taxes, insurance, savings plans, social security, or other benefits.

11. _ _ _ _ _ _   _ _ _ _ _ _ _ _
    l o c i a s   y i t u r c e s

A federal tax that appears as *FICA* on a check stub's payroll deductions.

12. _ _ _ _ _ _ _ _ _
    n e t e n d d e p

Any person who relies on another for financial support.

13. _ _ _ _ _ _ _
    r i m e m u p

The amount of money paid to cover a certain period of an insurance policy or plan.

14. _ _ _ _ _ _ _   _ _ _ _
    u i m m n i m   g e w a

The lowest amount per hour that employers can pay workers.

15. _ _ _ _ _ _ _ _
    o t y i r i n e s

The status of having worked a long time in a company or business.

Job Performance

Aiming for Job Success

◆ **Activity A**

Chapter 12

Name _____

Date _____ **Period** _____

For each example that follows, determine the work habit that the person is lacking and answer the questions in the space provided. Refer to pages 202-205 in your text.

1. Megan likes to talk during work hours with coworkers about disagreements with her supervisor. She often criticizes the company for its policies and decisions.

   A. Which work habit is lacking? _____

   _____

   B. What advice would you give? _____

   _____

   _____

2. Jordan frequently leaves 10 minutes early so he can catch the bus that travels closest to his house.

   A. Which work habit is lacking? _____

   _____

   B. What advice would you give? _____

   _____

   _____

3. Christi does not always wear the hard hat required on the construction site because it messes her hair.

   A. Which work habit is lacking? _____

   _____

   B. What advice would you give? _____

   _____

   _____

4. Austin does not like people telling him what to do, so he quietly does the job his way.

   A. Which work habit is lacking? _____

   _____

   B. What advice would you give? _____

   _____

   _____

(Continued)

Name_____

5. Amanda calls her boyfriend often from the office when work slows down.

    A. Which work habit is lacking? _____

    _____

    B. What advice would you give? _____

    _____

    _____

6. Angela turned down an opportunity for advanced training because it interfered with her bowling night.

    A. Which work habit is lacking? _____

    _____

    B. What advice would you give? _____

    _____

    _____

7. Kelly's desk is always piled high with papers. She can rarely find what she needs.

    A. Which work habit is lacking? _____

    _____

    B. What advice would you give? _____

    _____

    _____

8. Melissa occasionally uses a few of the company's stamps on her personal letters.

    A. Which work habit is lacking? _____

    _____

    B. What advice would you give? _____

    _____

    _____

9. Tyler goes out of his way not to do more work than is absolutely required.

    A. Which work habit is lacking? _____

    _____

    B. What advice would you give? _____

    _____

    _____

10. Instead of precisely measuring all ingredients at her cafeteria job, Adrian sometimes guesses rather than taking the time to locate the correct measuring tool.

    A. Which work habit is lacking? _____

    _____

    B. What advice would you give? _____

    _____

    _____

Attitudes Affect Performance

◆ **Activity B**

Chapter 12

Name _____

Date _____ Period _____

In your own words, explain how the following work attitudes may affect a person's success as a student and as an employee. Then answer the questions that follow.

Positive Attitudes	Positive Performance
1. Being friendly and courteous	Student example: Employee example:
2. Being enthusiastic and sharing enthusiasm	Student example: Employee example:
3. Practicing self-motivation	Student example: Employee example:
4. Being cooperative	Student example: Employee example:
5. Being honest and trustworthy	Student example: Employee example:

(Continued)

Name_____

6. What is an attitude? _____
    _____

7. Is an attitude a human resource? Explain. _____
    _____
    _____
    _____
    _____
    _____
    _____
    _____

Making the Workplace Safe

◆ **Activity C**

Chapter 12

Name_____

Date _____ Period _____

For each unsafe condition listed, write one way to prevent the condition or protect workers from it. Then answer the questions that follow.

Unsafe Conditions	Prevention and Protection Measures
1. Dangerous fumes	
2. Slippery conditions	
3. Dangerous equipment without safety guards	
4. Cords and boxes left in walkways	
5. Extension cords lying near water	
6. Tools left overhead on open shelves	
7. High frequency sounds	
8. Tall, unstable stack of heavy items	
9. Hot cooking oil left unattended on the range	
10. Piles of oily rags	

(Continued)

Name_____

11. List five jobs that involve high safety concerns. For each job, explain one of the risks.

    A. Job 1: _____

    _____

    _____

    B. Job 2: _____

    _____

    _____

    C. Job 3: _____

    _____

    _____

    D. Job 4: _____

    _____

    _____

    E. Job 5: _____

    _____

    _____

12. If you were the owner of a fastfood restaurant, what safety procedures would your employees need to know? Explain. _____

    _____

    _____

    _____

    _____

    _____

    _____

    _____

Clues to Good Health

◆ **Activity D**

Chapter 12

Name_____

Date _____ Period _____

If a statement is *true*, write true in the blank. If a statement is false, change the underlined word(s) to make the statement true and write the correct word(s) in the blank.

_____ 1. A <u>balanced</u> diet is one that provides all of the necessary nutrients needed for a healthy body.

_____ 2. Fats, oils, and sweets belong in the <u>bottom</u> group of the Food Guide Pyramid.

_____ 3. <u>One</u> food can provide all the nutrients needed daily.

_____ 4. Foods that are high in fats, sugar, and salt, but low in nutrients, are called <u>junk</u> foods.

_____ 5. Cutting calories and exercising more often usually causes a weight <u>gain</u>.

_____ 6. The <u>fewest</u> number of servings in everyone's diet should come from the bread, cereal, rice, and pasta group.

_____ 7. Diets <u>high</u> in fat, saturated fat, and cholesterol are related to health problems, such as obesity and heart disease.

_____ 8. A healthy diet is <u>low</u> in grain products, fruits, and vegetables.

_____ 9. The <u>Food Guide Pyramid</u> is a 10-point plan for good health that applies to people of all ages.

_____ 10. <u>Fewer</u> accidents occur on the job when people are well rested.

_____ 11. Most young people need at least <u>six</u> hours of sleep nightly.

_____ 12. <u>Regular</u> exercise helps you feel and look better.

_____ 13. Exercise <u>increases</u> job-related stress.

_____ 14. Both smoking and smokeless tobacco contain <u>nicotine</u>, an addictive chemical.

_____ 15. The senses of taste and smell <u>increase</u> with smoking.

_____ 16. Many businesses and public buildings <u>ban</u> smoking on the premises.

_____ 17. Many <u>fires</u> are caused by careless smokers.

_____ 18. Smoking is a very <u>inexpensive</u> habit.

_____ 19. <u>Drugs</u> are chemical substances that cause physical, emotional, or mental changes in people.

_____ 20. Possessing, selling, or using <u>illegal</u> drugs is a serious criminal offense.

_____ 21. Alcohol <u>enhances</u> mental processes.

(Continued)

Name_____

_____22. Using alcohol or <u>drugs</u> on the job can result in immediate dismissal.

_____23. Tranquilizers and diet pills are <u>illegal</u> drugs that are often abused.

_____24. Mentally healthy people have a <u>positive</u> self-image.

_____25. Good <u>physical</u> health is closely related to good mental health.

Job Evaluation and Change

Writing Employee Evaluations

◆ **Activity A**

Chapter 13

Name _____

Date _____ **Period** _____

Imagine you are an employer who must write a performance review for three workers doing the same job. *Employee 1* does the job exceptionally well, *Employee 2* is average, and *Employee 3* is failing. Name a job you know well and assume this is the job they hold. List all job responsibilities. Then write evaluations to match the performance levels of the imaginary employees.

Job title: _____

(Name a job that you know well.)

Job responsibilities: _____

(List as many as you can.)

_____

_____

_____

_____

_____

Performance Evaluation of Employee 1

_____

_____

_____

_____

_____

_____

_____

_____

_____

_____

(Continued)

Name_____

Performance Evaluation of Employee 2

_____
_____
_____
_____
_____
_____
_____
_____
_____
_____
_____
_____

Performance Evaluation of Employee 3

_____
_____
_____
_____
_____
_____
_____
_____
_____
_____
_____
_____

Facing Job-Loss Challenges

Name_____

Date _____ Period _____

Read the following job situations and explain how you would react if you found yourself in similar circumstances.

Case 1

Andy and Karen are newlyweds who, together, hold four jobs and attend college. Karen lost her full-time job as a paralegal and now must work full-time as a loan company clerk and part-time as a bookkeeper to equal her former salary. Andy works as a part-time law office clerk on weekdays and as an auctioneer on weekends, but barely earns enough money to pay the rent. Time and money seem to be big problems in their lives.

I would do the following in this situation:

_____
_____
_____
_____
_____
_____
_____
_____
_____
_____
_____
_____
_____
_____

Case 2

Mark left his job as a senior manager because his company was bought by another, and his views clashed with those of the new owners. He has a much more satisfying job, but he earns far less money. His wife, Deena, works full-time as a preschool teacher. Mark realizes that he is not making enough money to send his twin sons to college next year, even with his wife's income.

I would do the following in this situation:

_____
_____
_____
_____
_____
_____
_____
_____
_____
_____
_____
_____
_____

(Continued)

Name _____

Case 3

Mario was terminated from his full-time job along with 20 other employees because of a company reorganization. One week ago, the 25-year-old held a well-paying job that made use of his computer repair skills. He has looked for a similar job for two months with no success. To complicate matters, he is scheduled to be married in three months and worries about the plans already made, which he now cannot afford.

I would do the following in this situation:

_____
_____
_____
_____
_____
_____
_____
_____
_____
_____
_____
_____

Case 4

Maria lost her job due to the company's pending bankruptcy. Earlier in her career she lost a job, but found another relatively quickly. It has been four months and she still sees no sign of a good-paying job anytime soon. She is considering not wasting any more time searching and just withdrawing from the job market until business conditions improve.

I would do the following in this situation:

_____
_____
_____
_____
_____
_____
_____
_____
_____
_____
_____
_____

Job Evaluation Scramble

◆ **Activity C**

Chapter 13

Name_____

Date _____ **Period** _____

Unscramble the letters of the following words in the space provided. Then use the terms to compose an imaginary story about a worker and circle the ten terms in your story.

1. nobatyopirar dipore _____

2. lamorf telanuvaio _____

3. minaforl laenitovau_____

4. tocs-fo-vgiiln asrie _____

5. itrem ypa eisar _____

6. ronpomtoi_____

7. alelart rrceae vemo _____

8. emgerr_____

9. naevecers pya _____

10. terlet fo gotinarisen _____

A Worker's Story

Once upon a time, _____

_____

_____

_____

_____

_____

_____

_____

_____

_____

_____

_____

_____

_____

_____

_____

_____

_____

(Continued)

Name_____

_____

_____

_____

_____

_____

_____

_____

_____

_____

_____

_____

_____

_____

_____

_____

_____

Considering a Job Change

◆ **Activity D**

Chapter 13

Name _____

Date _____ Period _____

Decide if each statement below is a good or poor reason for changing jobs, and write its number in the appropriate space below. Then answer the question that follows.

1. There are constant conflicts with several coworkers at the current job.
2. The other job involves less work.
3. The other job involves more work.
4. The other job involves more interesting work.
5. The current job offers no opportunities for advancement.
6. Everyone at the current job can do the work better than you.
7. Additional training, involving 10 hours per week on weekends for four months at company expense, is needed to keep the current job.
8. Due to a money-losing year for the industry, everyone at the current job will see a five percent cut in pay for at least one year.
9. The other job offers better work hours and conditions.
10. The current job has too many rules and regulations.
11. The current job enforces the no-drugs-or-alcohol policy too strictly.
12. The current job bans cigarette smoking on all company premises, even the parking lot.
13. The current job is with a company so new that it lacks an employee policy.
14. The other job has all the newest, most sophisticated equipment in the profession.
15. The current job allows only five vacation days during the first year, while the new job allows 10.

Good Reasons for Changing Jobs   **Poor Reasons for Changing Jobs**

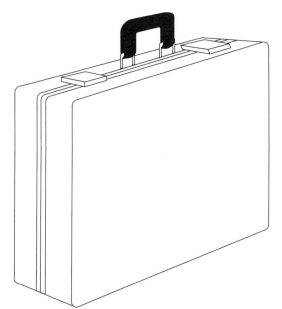   

(Continued)

Name_____

16. How long do you think an employee should stay with a job before considering leaving for a new job? Explain._____

_____

_____

_____

_____

_____

_____

_____

_____

_____

_____

_____

_____

_____

_____

_____

Careers in Business and Marketing

Job Description Challenge

◆ **Activity A**

Chapter 14

Name _____

Date _____ **Period** _____

Match the job descriptions in Column A with the job titles in Column B.

Column A

_____ 1. Prepares and serves food to gatherings in social centers, country clubs, and meeting halls.

_____ 2. Supervises food purchasing, preparation, and service in hospitals, nursing homes, and schools.

_____ 3. Assists companies with developing products that consumers want.

_____ 4. Works with the public to meet their lodging and travel-related needs.

_____ 5. Helps customers select merchandise, handles sales transactions, and keeps shelves stocked with merchandise.

_____ 6. Selects and purchases clothing merchandise, such as sportswear or children's wear, for a department in one or more retail stores.

_____ 7. Coordinates the operation of retail departments or stores and is responsible for the staff, merchandise displays, special promotions, and profits.

_____ 8. Stays informed of current fashion trends and works with retail stores to present a unified image.

_____ 9. Helps to sell the latest clothing by wearing and presenting it at fashion shows, stores, and trade shows.

_____ 10. Studies consumer buying trends.

Column B

A. banquet manager

B. consumer affairs specialists

C. fashion coordinator

D. fashion model

E. hotel manager

F. institutional foodservice director

G. marketing research analyst

H. merchandise manager

I. retail fashion buyer

J. retail sales associate

Interviewing a Professional

◆ **Activity B**

Chapter 14

Name _____

Date _____ **Period** _____

Select a job described in this chapter that interests you and interview a person who holds this or a similar job. Conduct the interview in person or by phone. Record his or her answers to the following questions.

1. What is your job title? _____

2. How long have you worked in this position? _____

3. What are the responsibilities of your job? _____

   _____

   _____

   _____

4. Why did you select this position? _____

   _____

   _____

   _____

5. What previous work or volunteer experience prepared you for the position? _____

   _____

   _____

   _____

6. What education and training did you obtain for this position? _____

   _____

   _____

   _____

7. What aspects of the job do you enjoy most? _____

   _____

   _____

8. Would you select a different career path if you could start over? _____

   _____

   _____

9. What advice would you give to someone considering this occupation? _____

   _____

   _____

   _____

   _____

   _____

   _____

Whom Would You Hire?

◆ **Activity C**

Chapter 14

Name_____

Date _____ Period _____

Imagine that you are the hiring manager for a company that needs the right person for a new position. Your assignment is to finish the want ad below, but before you can, you must decide what type of candidate to seek. Based on the information provided in the want ad, determine the qualities that person will need to do the job well and describe the ideal candidate on the next page. Then complete the want ad by summarizing the important points in your notes.

Want Ad

XYZ, Inc., a leading manufacturer of bathroom and kitchen tile, seeks an individual to fill a new position, that reports to the company president. Job responsibilities will include recommending product improvements, new designs, new product uses, and new methods of promoting the products and the company.

The individual should have:

_____

_____

_____

_____

_____

_____

_____

_____

_____

_____

_____

_____

_____

_____

_____

_____

_____

_____

_____

_____

_____

_____

Send resume to: MDM 437, Tribune, Chicago, IL 60611.

(Continued)

Name_____

My Notes Describing
the Ideal Job Candidate

Educational background: _____

_____

_____

_____

_____

Work experience and accomplishments: _____

_____

_____

_____

_____

_____

_____

_____

_____

_____

Communication skills: _____

_____

_____

_____

_____

Leadership qualities: _____

_____

_____

Work habits: _____

_____

_____

Special talents: _____

_____

_____

Learning About Jobs

◆ **Activity D**

Chapter 14

Name _____

Date _____ Period _____

Jobs vary greatly from one to another and some of the qualities that make them different are identified here. For each box, list three jobs from the chapter that share that quality. Then answer the questions that follow.

Jobs involving teamwork
1.
2.
3.

Jobs involving writing
1.
2.
3.

Jobs involving independent work
1.
2.
3.

Jobs involving outdoor work
1.
2.
3.

Jobs involving tools
1.
2.
3.

Jobs indoors with nonoffice settings
1.
2.
3.

(Continued)

Name_____

Jobs requiring frequent travel
1.
2.
3.

Jobs discovering new products
1.
2.
3.

Jobs with nontraditional work hours
1.
2.
3.

Jobs requiring creativity
1.
2.
3.

Jobs involving teaching
1.
2.
3.

Jobs that serve or help people
1.
2.
3.

Which three job qualities (appearing here as headings in the boxes) appeal most to you?

1. _____

2. _____

3. _____

Does your career plan include a job with the three qualities listed above? Explain. _____

_____

_____

Create a Career Ladder

◆ **Activity E**

Chapter 14

Name_____

Date _____ Period _____

Select a professional position described in this chapter that requires a bachelor's degree and create a career ladder for it. Following the directions below, write your responses on the appropriate steps of the ladder.

1. Write the title of the job you selected on top of the ladder at *A*.

2. Identify a job requiring advanced training that would be good preparation for *A*. Write it at *B*.

3. Identify an entry-level position that would be good preparation for *A*. Write it at *C*.

4. Identify a hobby or volunteer work that would be good preparation for *A*. Write it at *D*.

5. Identify a high school course that would prepare a person for *A*. Write it at *E*.

6. Identify an important personal trait for individuals considering *A*. Write it at *F*.

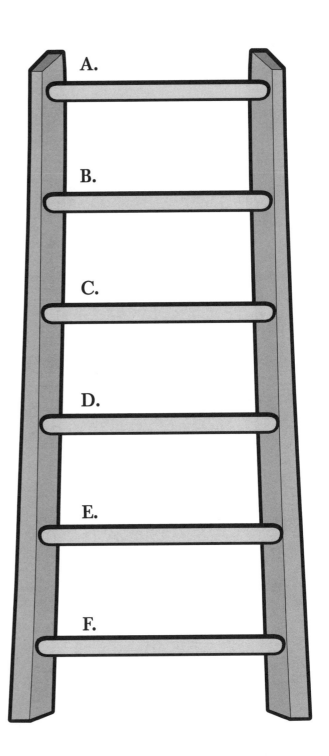

A.

B.

C.

D.

E.

F.

Future Trends and Careers

◆ **Activity F**

Chapter 14

Name_____

Date _____ **Period** _____

The trends observed today will affect the career opportunities in family and consumer sciences tomorrow. For each trend listed, name at least two business-related career areas that should grow as a result.

Trends	Career Opportunities Likely to Increase
More dual-career families	1.
	2.
Longer life span	1.
	2.
Interest in home improvement	1.
	2.
Increased travel	1.
	2.
More meals eaten away from home	1.
	2.
Money-management challenges	1.
	2.

Careers in Education and Communications

Clues to Educator Occupations

◆ **Activity A**

Chapter 15

Name_____

Date _____ Period _____

If a statement is true, write *true* in the blank. If a statement is false, change the underlined word(s) to make the statement true and write the correct word in the blank.

_____ 1. Family and consumer sciences preschool educators help <u>teens</u> make the change from home to group learning.

_____ 2. The main job of the <u>preschool</u> teacher is helping children learn to interact socially with other children.

_____ 3. Family and consumer sciences classes often begin in fifth grade and are usually <u>exploratory</u>.

_____ 4. Teaching introductory and advanced family and consumer sciences courses begins at the <u>college</u> level.

_____ 5. High school teachers are also called <u>secondary</u> teachers.

_____ 6. <u>Secondary</u> teachers of family and consumer sciences prepare students to handle the many responsibilities of family, job, and future life roles.

_____ 7. <u>Secondary</u> teaching positions in family and consumer sciences are available in vo-tech schools, two-year community colleges, four-year colleges, and universities.

_____ 8. The usual number of areas in family and consumer sciences on which college professors focus is <u>three</u>.

_____ 9. Continuing education teachers organize and teach programs for <u>adults</u>.

_____ 10. Most family and consumer sciences courses taught in adult education classes focus on the interests and needs that exist in the <u>nation</u>.

_____ 11. Educators in a vo-tech school teach <u>occupational</u> family and consumer sciences courses.

_____ 12. Teachers in nonschool settings who work with the U.S. Department of Agriculture and land-grant universities are called cooperative <u>planning</u> specialists.

_____ 13. Extension Service personnel generally report to <u>state</u> offices and use their training in family and consumer sciences to work with the local youth, adults, and seniors.

_____ 14. The <u>primary</u> job of an extension agent is to develop programs that meet the needs of people in his or her region.

_____ 15. Textbook authors are <u>in-school</u> examples of educator careers in family and consumer sciences.

Launching a Communications Career

◆ **Activity B**

Chapter 15

Name_____

Date _____ Period _____

Imagine you are a reporter for a teen magazine, assigned to write an article on how teens earn, spend, and think about money. You plan to interview at least 10 teens to get the information for the story. First, you must develop five questions to use in your interviews and decide how to make your story special.

1. Write five interview questions that will help you develop a story explaining how teens earn, spend, and think about money. (Assume that you already know the name and identity of the people you will interview.)

   A. _____

   _____

   _____

   _____

   _____

   _____

   B. _____

   _____

   _____

   _____

   C. _____

   _____

   _____

   _____

   D. _____

   _____

   _____

   E. _____

   _____

   _____

   _____

2. What will you do to make your article special, that is, an article that readers will want to read and save? _____

   _____

   _____

   _____

   _____

Learning About Jobs

◆ **Activity C**

Chapter 15

Name _____

Date _____ Period _____

Jobs vary greatly from one to another and some of the qualities that make them different are identified here. For each box, list three jobs from the chapter that share that quality. Then answer the questions that follow.

Jobs focusing on youth
1.
2.
3.

Jobs involving teamwork
1.
2.
3.

Jobs focusing on seniors
1.
2.
3.

Jobs involving computers
1.
2.
3.

Jobs involving independent work
1.
2.
3.

Jobs indoors with nonoffice settings
1.
2.
3.

(Continued)

Name_____

Jobs requiring frequent travel

1.

2.

3.

Jobs focusing on discoveries

1.

2.

3.

Jobs with nontraditional work hours

1.

2.

3.

Jobs requiring creativity

1.

2.

3.

Jobs focusing on current events

1.

2.

3.

Jobs that serve or help people

1.

2.

3.

Which three job qualities (appearing here as headings in the boxes) appeal most to you?

1. _____

2. _____

3. _____

Has your career preference changed, even slightly, from what you expressed in Chapter 14? Explain.

_____

_____

Whom Would You Hire?

◆ **Activity D**

Chapter 15

Name_____

Date _____ Period _____

Imagine that you are the hiring manager for a company that needs the right person for a new position. Your assignment is to finish the want ad below, but before you can, you must decide what type of candidate to seek. Based on the information provided in the want ad, determine the qualities that person will need to do the job well and describe the ideal candidate on the next page. Then complete the want ad by summarizing the important points in your notes.

Want Ad

XYZ Inc., a leading insurance company, seeks a full-time teacher/director to establish a new, on-site facility and program that will offer preschool services to the children of the company's employees. Job responsibilities will include designing the center, hiring appropriate staff, developing creative programs, and managing the budget.

The individual should have:

_____

_____

_____

_____

_____

_____

_____

_____

_____

_____

_____

_____

_____

_____

_____

_____

_____

_____

_____

_____

_____

Send resume to: MDM 437, Tribune, Chicago, IL 60611.

(Continued)

Name _____

My Notes Describing
the Ideal Job Candidate

Educational background: _____

_____

_____

_____

_____

Work experience and accomplishments: _____

_____

_____

_____

_____

_____

_____

_____

_____

_____

_____

_____

Communication skills: _____

_____

_____

_____

_____

_____

Leadership qualities: _____

_____

_____

Work habits: _____

_____

_____

Special talents: _____

_____

_____

Interviewing a Professional

◆ **Activity E**

Chapter 15

Name_____

Date _____ **Period** _____

Select a job described in this chapter that interests you and interview a person who holds this or a similar job. Conduct the interview in person or by phone. Record his or her answers to the following questions.

1. What is your job title? _____

2. How long have you worked in this position? _____

3. What are the responsibilities of your job?_____
   _____
   _____
   _____

4. Why did you select this position?_____
   _____
   _____
   _____

5. What previous work or volunteer experience prepared you for the position? _____
   _____
   _____
   _____

6. What education and training did you obtain for this position?_____
   _____
   _____
   _____

7. What aspects of the job do you enjoy most?_____
   _____
   _____

8. Would you select a different career path if you could start over?_____
   _____
   _____

9. What advice would you give to someone considering this occupation? _____
   _____
   _____
   _____
   _____
   _____
   _____

Create a Career Ladder

◆ **Activity F**   Name_____

   Chapter 15   Date _____ Period _____

Select a professional position described in this chapter that requires a bachelor's degree and create a career ladder for it. Following the directions below, write your responses on the appropriate steps of the ladder.

1. Write the title of the job you selected on top of the ladder at *A*.

2. Identify a job requiring advanced training that would be good preparation for *A*. Write it at *B*.

3. Identify an entry-level position that would be good preparation for *A*. Write it at *C*.

4. Identify a hobby or volunteer work that would be good preparation for *A*. Write it at *D*.

5. Identify a high school course that would prepare a person for *A*. Write it at *E*.

6. Identify an important personal trait for individuals considering *A*. Write it at *F*.

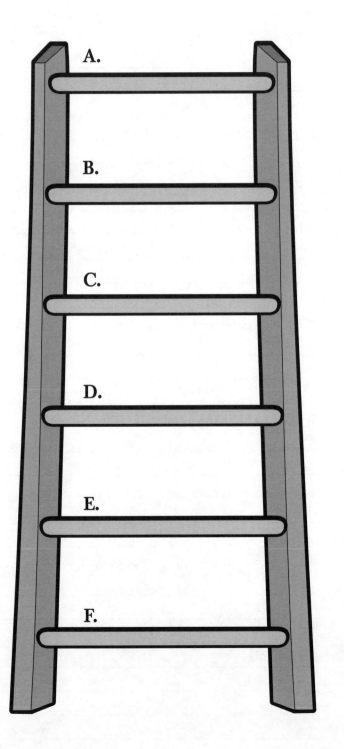

A.

B.

C.

D.

E.

F.

Careers in Human Services

Job Description Challenge

◆ **Activity A**

Chapter 16

Name _____

Date _____ **Period** _____

Match the job descriptions in Column A with the job titles in Column B.

Column A

_____ 1. Cares for children in group day care programs while parents work.

_____ 2. Works as a child development specialist by organizing special programs for children and young people.

_____ 3. Plans, organizes, and directs activities that help people enjoy their leisure time.

_____ 4. Leads and instructs campers in various forms of recreation.

_____ 5. Is a member of a professional team that provides health and social services to people with special needs.

_____ 6. Provides cleaning services in homes, offices, and businesses, according to an agreed schedule.

_____ 7. Helps people with disabilities learn to live independently.

_____ 8. Provides most of the routine care for residents of nursing homes.

_____ 9. Helps families, couples, and individuals deal with personal, family, and social problems.

_____ 10. Completes an internship and attains an M.S.W. before working to improve the quality of life of individuals and families in need.

Column B

A. camp counselor

B. child care worker

C. children's program director

D. counselor

E. geriatric aide

F. home health aide

G. housekeeper

H. recreation director

I. rehabilitation worker

J. social worker

Interviewing a Professional

◆ **Activity B**   **Name** _____

  Chapter 16   **Date** _____ **Period** _____

Select a child care job described in this chapter that interests you and interview a person who holds this or a similar job. Conduct the interview in person or by phone. Record his or her answers to the following questions.

1. What is your job title? _____

2. How long have you worked in this position? _____

3. What are the responsibilities of your job?_____

   _____

   _____

   _____

4. Why did you select this position?_____

   _____

   _____

   _____

5. What previous work or volunteer experience prepared you for the position? _____

   _____

   _____

   _____

6. What education and training did you obtain for this position?_____

   _____

   _____

   _____

7. What aspects of the job do you enjoy most?_____

   _____

   _____

8. Would you select a different career path if you could start over?_____

   _____

   _____

9. What advice would you give to someone considering this occupation? _____

   _____

   _____

   _____

   _____

   _____

Whom Would You Hire?

◆ **Activity C**

Chapter 16

Name _____

Date _____ **Period** _____

Imagine that you are the hiring manager for Camp Eagle Point, a camp dedicated to inspiring self-esteem in teen boys who have been in trouble with local law enforcement agencies. Your assignment is to finish the want ad below, but before you can, you must decide what type of candidate to seek. Based on the information provided in the want ad, determine the qualities that person will need to do the job well and describe the ideal candidate on the next page. Then complete the want ad by summarizing the important points in your notes.

Want Ad

Camp Eagle Point, a unique year-round camp facility devoted exclusively to creating life-changing experiences for troubled teens, seeks an energetic Assistant Director to work with boys, ages 13 to 17. Besides leading the daily activities (canoeing, swimming, hiking, craft-making, etc.), the ideal candidate will also inspire youths during their 10-week stay to recognize their inner worth, explore life options, develop positive goals, and cooperate well with others.

The individual should have:

_____

_____

_____

_____

_____

_____

_____

_____

_____

_____

_____

_____

_____

_____

_____

_____

_____

_____

_____

Send resume to: MDM 437, Tribune, Chicago, IL 60611.

(Continued)

Name_____

My Notes Describing
the Ideal Job Candidate

Educational background: _____

_____

_____

_____

_____

Work experience and accomplishments: _____

_____

_____

_____

_____

_____

_____

_____

_____

_____

Communication skills: _____

_____

_____

_____

_____

Leadership qualities: _____

_____

_____

Work habits: _____

_____

_____

Special talents: _____

_____

_____

Is This Job for You?

◆ **Activity D**

Chapter 16

Name _____

Date _____ **Period** _____

As the numbers of people living longer grows, the need increases for assistants to help seniors in their homes or in special rehabilitation or living facilities. To determine if this type of job appeals to you, check the column that best reflects your response to each statement below. Then answer the following question.

	Yes	Sometimes	No
1. I like to help older people who are in need.			
2. I am usually quite happy and cheerful.			
3. I like to hear others tell how life was different many years ago.			
4. I am good at determining what needs to be done and doing it.			
5. It does not bother me if I do more than my share of work.			
6. I am always honest, trustworthy, and patient.			
7. It does not bother me to be around weak or sickly people.			
8. I am always concerned about making life more pleasant for older people.			
9. I get a great deal of personal satisfaction in helping older people.			

10. Would you like to be a companion for the elderly? Explain. _____

_____

_____

_____

_____

_____

_____

_____

_____

_____

_____

Create a Career Ladder

◆ **Activity E**

Chapter 16

Name_____

Date _____ Period _____

Select a professional position described in this chapter that requires a bachelor's degree and create a career ladder for it. Following the directions below, write your responses on the appropriate steps of the ladder.

1. Write the title of the job you selected on top of the ladder at *A*.

2. Identify a job requiring advanced training that would be good preparation for *A*. Write it at *B*.

3. Identify an entry-level position that would be good preparation for *A*. Write it at *C*.

4. Identify a hobby or volunteer work that would be good preparation for *A*. Write it at *D*.

5. Identify a high school course that would prepare a person for *A*. Write it at *E*.

6. Identify an important personal trait for individuals considering *A*. Write it at *F*.

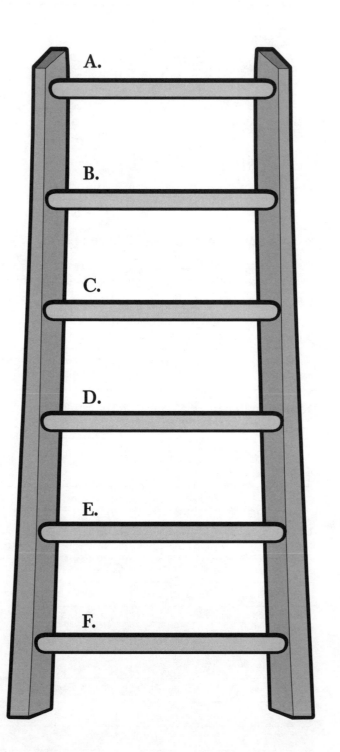

A.

B.

C.

D.

E.

F.

Evaluating Careers in Human Services

◆ **Activity F**

Chapter 16

Name _____

Date _____ Period _____

All careers have satisfactions and problems, but the challenge in making a good career choice is recognizing which jobs offer many satisfactions but very few problems. For each career category that follows, list possible satisfactions and problems in the appropriate space. You may write your own thoughts and/or consult with those who are employed in the field.

Child Care Services

Satisfactions	Problems

Hospitality and Recreation Work

Satisfactions	Problems

Homemaker and Home Health Services

Satisfactions	Problems

(Continued)

Name_____

Rehabilitation Services

Satisfactions	Problems

Geriatric Services

Satisfactions	Problems

Counseling

Satisfactions	Problems

Social Work

Satisfactions	Problems

Careers in Science and Technology

Clues to Science and Technology Jobs

◆ **Activity A**

Chapter 17

Name_____

Date _____ Period _____

If a statement is true, write *true* in the blank. If a statement is false, change the underlined word(s) to make the statement true and write the correct word(s) in the blank.

_____ 1. <u>Technology</u> is the application of knowledge to solve problems and improve and extend human capabilities.

_____ 2. <u>Dietetics</u> is the study of how your body uses the food you eat.

_____ 3. A <u>nutritionist</u> is a member of a health care team who evaluates patients' nutritional needs.

_____ 4. <u>Nutritionists</u> study the way the body digests and uses food.

_____ 5. <u>Food science</u> is the study of producing, processing, storing, preserving, utilizing, and evaluating food.

_____ 6. A <u>formula</u> is a working recipe for a food product.

_____ 7. <u>Quality control</u> inspectors check the food products in a manufacturing plant at all stages to meet precise standards and specifications.

_____ 8. In addition to preparing food, the work of a <u>baker</u> often involves developing recipes, planning menus, ordering food, and overseeing the entire foodservice staff.

_____ 9. <u>Bakers</u> work in supermarkets, restaurants, bakeries, and baking companies.

_____ 10. <u>Food</u> research and development scientists work with fibers, fabrics, dyes, and textile finishes.

_____ 11. In the textile industry, examples of <u>production</u> workers include sample makers, pattern makers, and pattern graders.

_____ 12. <u>Finishers</u> are workers who prepare fabric for cutting by carefully stacking many layers of fabric.

_____ 13. New garments are finished by <u>machine</u> sewers who specialize in one technique, such as attaching buttons, hooks, eyes, or special trims.

_____ 14. <u>Product managers</u> in the apparel production industry coordinate and oversee all aspects of manufacturing a line of products, such as men's winter outerwear.

_____ 15. <u>Production managers</u> in the apparel production industry estimate plant costs, schedule the work flow, and hire and train the workers.

_____ 16. In the dry cleaning industry, the people who inspect garments for stains and damage after the customer brings them in are called <u>spotters</u>.

_____ 17. Textile <u>finishers</u> work to preserve historical garments and fabrics.

Interviewing a Professional

Select a job involving food, nutrition, and wellness described in this chapter that interests you. Interview a person who holds this or a similar job. Conduct the interview in person or by phone. Record his or her answers to the following questions.

1. What is your job title? _____

2. How long have you worked in this position? _____

3. What are the responsibilities of your job?_____

   _____

   _____

   _____

4. Why did you select this position?_____

   _____

   _____

   _____

5. What previous work or volunteer experience prepared you for the position? _____

   _____

   _____

   _____

6. What education and training did you obtain for this position?_____

   _____

   _____

   _____

7. What aspects of the job do you enjoy most?_____

   _____

   _____

8. Would you select a different career path if you could start over?_____

   _____

   _____

9. What advice would you give to someone considering this occupation? _____

   _____

   _____

   _____

   _____

   _____

   _____

Whom Would You Hire?

◆ **Activity C**

Chapter 17

Name _____

Date _____ **Period** _____

Imagine that you are the hiring manager for LMN Corporation, a company that manufactures textiles for carpeting, upholstery, and drapery. Your assignment is to finish the want ad below, but before you can, you must decide what type of candidate to seek. Based on the information provided in the want ad, determine the qualities that person will need to do the job well and describe the ideal candidate on the next page. Then complete the want ad by summarizing the important points in your notes.

Want Ad

LMN Corporation, the number one company in fabrics for the home, seeks a textile technician to help develop new products and evaluate competing products. The ideal person will have excellent skills in communication, technical writing, and research. The position requires working closely with the sales staff and holding regular briefings on new products and features.

The individual should have:

_____

_____

_____

_____

_____

_____

_____

_____

_____

_____

_____

_____

_____

_____

_____

_____

_____

_____

_____

_____

Send resume to: MDM 437, Tribune, Chicago, IL 60611.

(Continued)

Name_____

My Notes Describing
the Ideal Job Candidate

Educational background: _____

_____

_____

_____

_____

Work experience and accomplishments: _____

_____

_____

_____

_____

_____

_____

_____

_____

_____

Communication skills: _____

_____

_____

_____

_____

Leadership qualities: _____

_____

_____

Work habits: _____

_____

_____

Special talents: _____

_____

_____

Learning About Jobs

◆ **Activity D**

Chapter 17

Name _____

Date _____ Period _____

Jobs vary greatly from one to another and some of the qualities that make them different are identified here. For each box, list three jobs from the chapter that share that quality. Then answer the questions that follow.

Jobs involving teamwork
1.
2.
3.

Jobs involving writing
1.
2.
3.

Jobs involving independent work
1.
2.
3.

Jobs involving factory work
1.
2.
3.

Jobs involving tools
1.
2.
3.

Jobs indoors with nonoffice settings
1.
2.
3.

(Continued)

_____Name

Jobs requiring frequent travel
1.
2.
3.

Jobs involving discovery
1.
2.
3.

Jobs with nontraditional work hours
1.
2.
3.

Jobs requiring creativity
1.
2.
3.

Jobs involving teaching
1.
2.
3.

Jobs that serve or help people
1.
2.
3.

Which three job qualities (appearing here as headings in the boxes) appeal most to you?

1. _____

2. _____

3. _____

Has your career preference changed, even slightly, from what you expressed in Chapter 15's activity? Explain. _____

_____

_____

Examining Personal Skills

◆ **Activity E**

Chapter 17

Name_____

Date _____ **Period** _____

List and describe below 10 positions discussed in this chapter and identify the personal skills and abilities that are needed for each.

Job Description	Skills and Abilities Needed
1. _____	
2. _____	
3. _____	
4. _____	
5. _____	
6. _____	
7. _____	
8. _____	
9. _____	
10. _____	

Create a Career Ladder

Name _____

Date _____ Period _____

Select a professional position described in this chapter that requires a bachelor's degree and create a career ladder for it. Following the directions below, write your responses on the appropriate steps of the ladder.

1. Write the title of the job you selected on top of the ladder at *A*.

2. Identify a job requiring advanced training that would be good preparation for *A*. Write it at *B*.

3. Identify an entry-level position that would be good preparation for *A*. Write it at *C*.

4. Identify a hobby or volunteer work that would be good preparation for *A*. Write it at *D*.

5. Identify a high school course that would prepare a person for *A*. Write it at *E*.

6. Identify an important personal trait for individuals considering *A*. Write it at *F*.

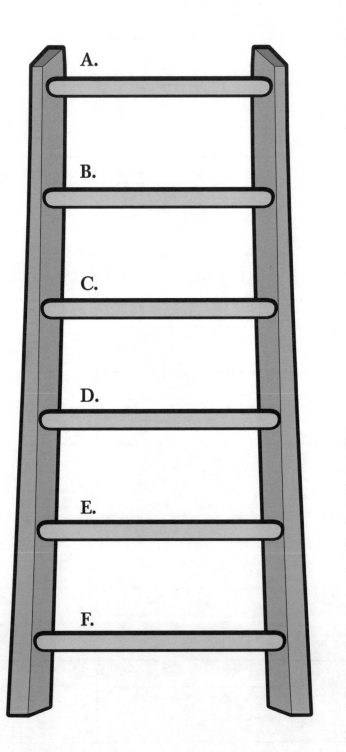

A.

B.

C.

D.

E.

F.

Careers in the Arts

Picture It

◆ **Activity A**

   Chapter 18

Name_____

Date _____ Period _____

Draw the picture that comes into your mind when you visualize an attractive product resulting from any activity involving food, clothing, textiles, or interior design.

The Artistic Side of Family and Consumer Sciences

Interviewing a Professional

◆ **Activity B**   **Name**_____

   Chapter 18   **Date** _____ **Period** _____

Select a job described in this chapter that interests you and interview a person who holds this or a similar job. Conduct the interview in person or by phone. Record his or her answers to the following questions.

1. What is your job title? _____

2. How long have you worked in this position? _____

3. What are the responsibilities of your job?_____

   _____

   _____

   _____

4. Why did you select this position?_____

   _____

   _____

   _____

5. What previous work or volunteer experience prepared you for the position? _____

   _____

   _____

   _____

6. What education and training did you obtain for this position?_____

   _____

   _____

   _____

7. What aspects of the job do you enjoy most?_____

   _____

   _____

8. Would you select a different career path if you could start over?_____

   _____

   _____

9. What advice would you give to someone considering this occupation? _____

   _____

   _____

   _____

   _____

   _____

Whom Would You Hire?

◆ **Activity C**

Chapter 18

Name _____

Date _____ **Period** _____

Imagine that you are the hiring manager for a mobile home manufacturer. Your assignment is to write the want ad below, but before you can, you must decide what type of candidate to seek. Based on the information provided in the want ad, determine the qualities that person will need to do the job well and describe the ideal candidate on the next page. Then complete the want ad by summarizing the important points in your notes.

Want Ad

A-1 Company, a small midwestern mobile home manufacturer, seeks a person who can design attractive, innovative, cost-efficient interiors for mobile homes. The ideal person must be versatile, assume many tasks, and have an extensive interior design background. Additionally, the person must be able to design small residential spaces to look fashionable and function efficiently.

The individual should have:

_____
_____
_____
_____
_____
_____
_____
_____
_____
_____
_____
_____
_____
_____
_____
_____
_____
_____
_____
_____
_____

Send resume to: MDM 437, Tribune, Chicago, IL 60611.

(Continued)

Name_____

My Notes Describing
the Ideal Job Candidate

Educational background: _____

_____

_____

_____

_____

Work experience and accomplishments: _____

_____

_____

_____

_____

_____

_____

_____

_____

_____

Communication skills: _____

_____

_____

_____

_____

Leadership qualities: _____

_____

_____

Work habits: _____

_____

_____

Special talents: _____

_____

_____

Job Description Challenge

◆ **Activity D**

Chapter 18

Name _____

Date _____ Period _____

Match the job descriptions in Column A with the job titles in Column B.

Column A

_____ 1. Creates new designs for fabrics used in wearing apparel, home furnishings, and commercial furnishings.

_____ 2. Chooses the color combinations that are used in textiles.

_____ 3. Coordinates the designs and colors used in textile production at the mills by staying alert to trends, fashion forecasts, and economic conditions.

_____ 4. Designs clothing and accessories.

_____ 5. Draws or sketches new fashions for retail stores, pattern companies, and advertising agencies.

_____ 6. Sews one-of-a-kind garments for others.

_____ 7. Researches, preserves, and displays historical clothing collections.

_____ 8. Helps people choose clothing and accessories that project their best image.

_____ 9. Decorates one or more rooms in a home according to customer specifications.

_____ 10 Helps clients choose the best lighting products and oversees their installation.

_____ 11. Designs attractive, functional kitchens.

_____ 12. Designs the interiors of large, public buildings, and selects and places furnishings.

_____ 13. Uses visual merchandising techniques to attractively display a store's image and merchandise.

_____ 14. Arranges food to produce appetizing effects for photos.

_____ 15. Blends good design principles with fresh and artificial floral arrangements.

Column B

A. commercial interior designer

B. costume curator

C. custom tailor

D. display artist

E. fashion designer

F. fashion illustrator

G. floral designer

H. food stylist

I. home lighting consultant

J. interior designer

K. kitchen planner

L. textile colorist

M. textile designer

N. textile stylist

O. wardrobe consultant

Create a Career Ladder

◆ **Activity E**

    Chapter 18

Name_____

Date _____ **Period** _____

Select a professional position described in this chapter that requires a bachelor's degree and create a career ladder for it. Following the directions below, write your responses on the appropriate steps of the ladder.

1. Write the title of the job you selected on top of the ladder at *A*.

2. Identify a job requiring advanced training that would be good preparation for *A*. Write it at *B*.

3. Identify an entry-level position that would be good preparation for *A*. Write it at *C*.

4. Identify a hobby or volunteer work that would be good preparation for *A*. Write it at *D*.

5. Identify a high school course that would prepare a person for *A*. Write it at *E*.

6. Identify an important personal trait for individuals considering *A*. Write it at *F*.

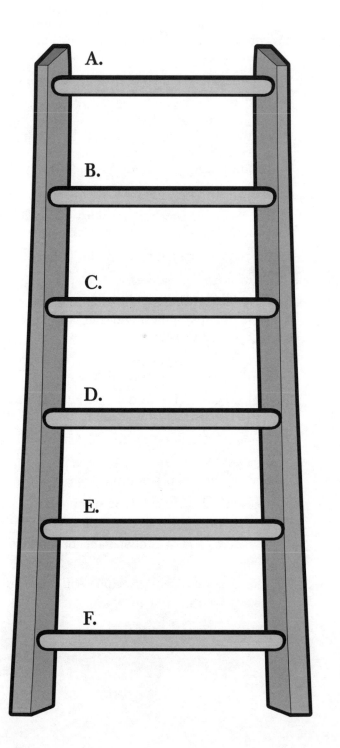

Looking Ahead

Name _____

Date _____ Period _____

Select 10 jobs discussed in the chapter that interest you most and write them on the lines below. For each, identify one trend likely to affect the job in the future and one skill or ability that will be necessary as a result. Then answer the question that follows.

Job Title	Future Trend	Skill or Ability Needed
1. _____		
2. _____		
3. _____		
4. _____		
5. _____		
6. _____		
7. _____		
8. _____		
9. _____		
10. _____		

(Continued)

Name_____

Which job discussed in this chapter interests you most? Explain why._____

_____

_____

_____

_____

_____

_____

_____

_____

_____

_____

_____

_____

_____

_____

_____

_____

A Career as an Entrepreneur

My Entrepreneurial Assessment

◆ **Activity A**

Chapter 19

Name_____

Date _____ Period _____

Review the statements below and place a check in the column that best describes you. Then answer the questions that follow.

Personal Checklist			
Characteristics	**Usually**	**Sometimes**	**Rarely**
1. I prefer to work rather than sit idle.			
2. Others tend to follow my lead.			
3. I enjoy setting long-term goals and completing them.			
4. I keep my school papers and personal records in excellent order.			
5. I like creating ideas.			
6. I like executing plans.			
7. I like competing.			
8. I like taking risks.			
9. I am friendly with everyone.			
10. I am very persistent.			
11. I carefully plan my work before I start.			
12. I like making difficult decisions.			
13. I communicate well face-to-face and on paper.			
14. I like confronting challenges.			
15. I have a high level of motivation and drive.			
16. I am willing to work when others are resting or playing.			
17. I enjoy turning problems into opportunities.			
18. I have a positive attitude.			
19. I like to match my ideas against the best.			
20. I like to succeed where others have failed.			

(Continued)

Name_____

21. Which of the entrepreneurial characteristics from the checklist best describe you?_____

_____

_____

_____

_____

22. Which of the characteristics from the checklist would you need to improve before you could consider a career as an entrepreneur?_____

_____

_____

_____

_____

_____

_____

_____

_____

_____

Interviewing an Entrepreneur

◆ **Activity B**

Chapter 19

Name_____

Date _____ **Period** _____

Interview a local entrepreneur in person or by phone. Identify the person's name and the name of his or her business. Then record that person's answers to the following questions.

Person interviewed: _____

Name of business: _____

1. How do you describe your business?_____

_____

_____

2. Is your business a sole proprietorship, partnership, or corporation? _____

_____

3. When you were a teen, was anyone in your family an independent business person? (If yes, explain.) __

_____

_____

_____

_____

4. What were your career plans as a teen? _____

_____

_____

_____

_____

5. How did you get into this business?_____

_____

_____

_____

_____

6. Who most influenced you as a business role model? Explain. _____

_____

_____

_____

_____

_____

(continued)

Name_____

7. What most prepared you for the work you do today?_____

_____

_____

_____

_____

_____

_____

8. Did your business begin where it is located today? (If no, explain.)_____

_____

_____

_____

9. How many hours a week do you work at your business?_____

10. What do you most like about having your own business?_____

_____

_____

_____

11. What do you least like about having your own business?_____

_____

_____

_____

_____

_____

12. What does success mean to you?_____

_____

_____

_____

_____

_____

_____

_____

13. What advice would you give to anyone considering their own business?_____

_____

_____

_____

_____

Examining Business Ownership

Name_____

Date _____ Period _____

List the advantages and disadvantages of the three ways to establish the legal ownership of a business. Then follow the directions on the next page.

Sole Proprietorship

Advantages	Disadvantages

Partnership

Advantages	Disadvantages

Corporation

Advantages	Disadvantages

(Continued)

Name_____

If you became an entrepreneur, name the type of business you would most likely pursue. _____

_____

_____

_____

_____

Identify the form of legal organization you would choose for that business and explain why. _____

_____

_____

_____

_____

_____

_____

_____

_____

_____

More Than a Summer Job

Name_____

Date _____ **Period** _____

Read the case study below and answer the questions that follow.

Case Study

To prepare for a summer job, Rick distributed over 500 flyers throughout the neighborhood in early April, advertising his lawn service business. Rick called his new business Executive Lawns, which provided lawn mowing and general yard maintenance and landscaping. Rick said, "I figured it would be a real challenge to start my own company. I thought I might even make more money in the summer than I could working for my dad. Besides, I like the idea of being my own boss."

Rick started the summer with the basic necessities for running the business. With his savings, he bought a new lawn mower ($320), a used lawn edger/trimmer ($90), and an assortment of garden tools (about $140). He was able to finish paying for them after two weeks of work.

Rick sees himself as a hard-working, honest, determined, innovative go-getter, and the success of his company seems to bear this out. Now with a full load of steady accounts, Rick says, "I spend as much time planning and scheduling as I do working, but I prefer to do this than work for someone else."

Rick's advice for anyone thinking about starting a business is to carefully plan everything first. "You have to think positively," he says, "and never give in to fears of failing because people are counting on you."

---

1. What do you feel is the key to Rick's success? _____

   _____

   _____

   _____

   _____

   _____

   _____

   _____

2. What personal skills does Rick possess that helped him to succeed?_____

   _____

   _____

   _____

   _____

   _____

   _____

   _____

(Continued)

Name_____

3. Is there anything that you think Rick should have done differently? Explain. _____

_____

_____

_____

_____

_____

_____

4. How can the experience of operating a summer job help Rick in the future? _____

_____

_____

_____

_____

_____

_____

_____